Contents

The Phonic Code	page 2
Notes on the Talisman 2 Series and Workbook	page 3
Front page for pupil's folder	page 5
Book 1 Reunited: phoneme 'ue'	page 7
Book 2 Trouble in the Woods: phonemes 'u' and 'o'	page 21
Book 3 Certain Death: phoneme 's'	page 41
Book 4 The Fossil: phoneme 'l'	page 57
Book 5 Legends of the Gorge: phoneme 'j'	page 71
Book 6 The Sphinx: phoneme 'f'	page 85
Book 7 Sticky Adventure: suffix 'cher'	page 99
Book 8 Dangerous Direction: suffix 'shun'	page 113
Book 9 Zak Tries Martial Arts: suffixes 'shul' and 'shus'	page 127
Book 10 The Dark Master's Vision: suffixes 'zhun' and 'zher'	page 149

The Phonic Code

Consonant Sound Spellings

'p'
- p hop
- pp happy

'v'
- v very
- ve have

'b'
- b big
- bb rabbit

'ch'
- ch chip
- tch match

'w'
- w wig
- wh when

'qu'
- qu queen

's'
- s   sip
- ss grass
- c   (eiy) cent
- ce voice
- se house
- st castle
- sc science

'g'
- g   rag
- gg juggle
- gh ghost

'y'
- y yes

'f'
- f   fat
- ff staff
- ph phone
- gh laugh
- ffe giraffe

'k'
- k   kite
- c   cat
- ck duck
- ch Christmas
- que antique
- q   Iraq

'm'
- m   man
- mm summer
- mb lamb
- mn Autumn

'ng'
- n   pink
- ng sing

'sh'
- sh shop
- ch machine
- s   sugar

'l'
- l   lip
- ll full
- le apple
- el travel
- il pupil
- al final
- ol idol

't'
- t   tin
- tt getting
- bt debt
- pt pterodactyl
- te granite

'j'
- j   jet
- g   (eiy) gentle
- ge barge
- dge judge
- dj adjust

'r'
- r   rat
- wr write
- rr carry
- rh rhino

'n'
- n   no
- nn planning
- kn know
- gn gnat
- pn pneumonia

'z'
- z   zip
- zz buzz
- s   is
- se choose
- ze snooze
- x   xylophone

'gz' 'x'
- x   exam

'h'
- h   hot
- wh whole

'ks' 'x'
- x   fox
- cc accept

'd'
- d   did
- ed grabbed
- dd muddle

'zh'
- s   leisure
- ge prestige
- z   seizure

'th'
- th moth
- th that (voiced)

Vowel Sound Spellings

'oe'
- o   most
- o-e   note
- oe   toe
- oa   boat
- ow   grow
- ough though
- ou   soul
- ew   sew

'a'
- a cat

'o'
- o   not
- a   was
- ou cough

'ie'
- i   wild
- ie   pie
- i-e like
- igh night
- y   dry
- eigh height

'ee'
- e   me
- ee   meet
- ea   seat
- e-e eve
- ie   chief
- y   funny
- ey   key
- ei   re(c)eive
- i   variation
- eo   people

'ae'
- a   table
- ai   rain
- a-e game
- ea   great
- ay   say
- ey   they
- ei   vein
- aigh straight
- eigh eight

'aw'
- au   fraud
- aw   lawn
- a   ball
- al   walk
- or   for
- our your
- ore more
- oor door
- oar board
- (w)ar warm
- ough fought
- augh daughter

'e'
- e   bed
- ea bread
- ai said
- ie friend
- eo leopard

'er'
- er   perk
- ur   turn
- ir   girl
- or   world
- ear learn
- our colour
- ar   collar
- re   centre
- yr   zephyr

'oo'
- oo   cook
- oul could
- u   put
- o   woman

'i'
- i in
- y myth

'u'
- u   tub
- ou touch
- a   about
- o   Monday
- oo blood

'ar'
- a   glass
- al calm
- ar jar
- er clerk
- ear heart

'ow'
- ow   cow
- ou   out
- ough drought

'oi'
- oi join
- oy boy

'ue'
- u-e mule
- u   pupil
- ew few
- ue cue

'air'
- air chair
- are dare
- ear bear
- eir their
- ere where
- ayor mayor
- ayer prayer
- ae   aeroplane

'oo'
- oo   boot
- ue   blue
- ew   grew
- u   super
- ui   suit
- u-e flute
- ou   soup
- oe   shoe
- o   do
- ough through

Phonic Books Ltd.

Notes on the Talisman 2 Series and Workbook

Talisman 2 Series

Introduction
The Talisman 2 Series continues from the Talisman 1 Series with the introduction of alternative spellings for more vowel and consonant sounds. Book 7 of the series introduces suffixes. To see the phonic progression of the series, see the table on page 4. The series includes ten books, each with a phonic focus. The workbook is based on the stories and includes a variety of activities to encourage the reader to practise reading and spelling, using the phonic knowledge and skills introduced in the books. Activities which develop comprehension and language skills are also included.

Suffixes
Book 7 introduces suffixes with complex spellings. At this point, they are taught as one syllable as they can be added to root words to make many long words in English. This enables the reader to read and spell many new difficult multisyllabic words. To see the introduction of suffixes and their spellings, see the table on page 4.

More text in the Talisman 2 Series
The Talisman 2 Series introduces more text to a page. Alternate pages have two paragraphs of text broken up by a small illustration. This is designed to motivate the reluctant reader to persevere and read a whole page of text.

Order of the books
Talisman 2 Series should be read in order. The phonic focus in each book becomes gradually more difficult, ending with complex suffixes.

Pronunciation
At the beginning of each book, there is a word list to help the reader learn the alternative spellings of the sounds and suffixes. Pronunciation of some sounds may vary, according to regional accents. The word lists may not always match the pronunciation of the pupil. This point should be discussed and the lists adapted to the pupil.

Blending, not guessing
Encourage the reader to use their phonic knowledge to blend the sounds fast throughout the word. If there are spellings they do not know, point to the part of the word that is new and tell them the sound. Then, get the pupil to blend the sound into the word. As they work through the Phonic Code, they will be able to use this phonic approach successfully with an increasing number of words.

Teaching alternative spellings
The English Phonic Code is complex. This series presents a number of alternative spellings for sounds and for suffixes. The teacher may need to introduce these spellings gradually if the pupil has difficulty learning all the alternative spellings at a time.

Splitting multisyllabic words
At the bottom of every page, a few multisyllabic words are split for the reader. This will enable the reader to tackle longer words independently. There are a number of ways to split multisyllabic words. The approach taken, in this series, is to split the word in the most 'reader-friendly' way.

New vocabulary

Each new book offers an opportunity to learn new vocabulary on the vocabulary page. This page explains the words as they appear in the context of the story. The teacher may wish to discuss additional meanings of the words with the pupil.

The workbook

This workbook complements the Talisman 2 series. Ten chapters in the workbook correlate to the ten books in the series. Each chapter offers activities based on the phonic focus of each of the books. Before reading the books, pupils would benefit from practising the knowledge and skills needed to read the book independently. This includes the word building, blending, reading and sorting activities which feature at the beginning of every chapter. Follow-up activities, such as comprehension, spelling, writing and the games, should be used after reading the texts. The teacher can select from the activities in each chapter to maintain interest and variety.

While most of the chapters of the workbook present alternative spellings for vowel sounds, consonant sounds and suffixes, chapters for Books 2, 3, and 5 include activities for spellings that represent alternative sounds. These exercises teach the pupil that he/she may need to try an alternative sound when reading certain graphemes e.g. <c> represents 'k' in <cat> and 's' in <cell>.

An instruction for every activity in the workbook appears at the bottom of each page.

Phonic sequence in the Talisman 2 Series: Books 1–10

Book	Title	Phonic focus	Spellings
Book 1	Reunited	'ue'	u-e, ue, ew, u
Book 2	Trouble in the Woods	'u' and 'o'	'u': ou, o, u and 'o': a, o, ou
Book 3	Certain Death	's'	s, ss, c, ce, se, sc, st
Book 4	The Fossil	'l'	l, ll, le, il, al, ol, el
Book 5	Legends of the Gorge	'j'	j, g, ge, dge, dj
Book 6	The Sphinx	'f'	f, ff, gh, ph
Book 7	Sticky Adventure	'cher'	ture
Book 8	Dangerous Direction	'shun'	tion, ssion, tian, sion, cian
Book 9	Zak Tries Martial Arts	'shul' and 'shus'	'shul': cial, tial and 'shus': tious, cious, ious
Book 10	The Dark Master's Vision	'zhun' and 'zher'	sion and sure

Talisman 2 Series Workbook

for Books 1-10

Name: _____

Pupils can use this page as a personalised front cover for their Talisman 2 Series work.
They may wish to decorate in each symbol in the talisman as they read the series.

Book 1: Reunited

Questions for discussion

Chapter 1

1. Why couldn't Zak fall asleep? (pg 1)
2. The old woman told him to 'resume the quest'. What does that mean? (pg 2)
3. How was the Dark Master going to make a new talisman for himself? (pg 3)

Chapter 2

1. Why do you think Grandpa was sad when he told Zak he had to save mankind? (pg 4)
2. Zak said the quest was futile. What did he mean? (pg 4)
3. Why do you think Mim needed to protect Grandpa? (pg 6)

Chapter 3

1. Why did Samson 'consume the food' hungrily? (pg 7)

Chapter 4

1. What did Zak use as fuel to make a fire? (pg 9)

Chapter 5

1. Why was Zak angry with the mule? (pg 10)

These questions can be discussed after reading the text. They are intended to develop speaking and listening skills and comprehension. This sheet may be photocopied by the purchaser. © Phonic Books Ltd. 2011.

Book 1: Blending and segmenting: 'ue'

new	n	ew			
due	☐	☐			
use	☐	☐	☐		
music	☐	☐	☐	☐	☐
few	☐	☐			
cue	☐	☐			
tube	☐	☐	☐		
tunic	☐	☐	☐	☐	☐
stew	☐	☐	☐		
rescue	☐	☐	☐	☐	☐
excuse	☐	☐	☐	☐	☐
funeral	☐	☐	☐	☐	☐
amuse	☐	☐	☐	☐	

Blend the sounds into a word. Segment the word into sounds by writing one sound in each square. Split vowel spellings (u–e) are represented by half squares linked together. This sheet may be photocopied by the purchaser. © Phonic Books Ltd. 2011.

Book 1: Reading and sorting words with 'ue' spellings

u	ue	u-e	ew

use	cue	new	music
cupid	accuse	pupil	nude
duty	attitude	tune	rescue
subdue	cube	refuse	knew
excuse	stew	tunic	ridicule
few	puny	amuse	cute
Cuba	abuse	dew	funeral
mule	due	hue	fuse

Photocopy this page onto card and cut out the words. Read and sort the cards out according to the 'ue' headings at the top of the page. This sheet may be photocopied by the purchaser. © Phonic Books Ltd. 2011.

Book 1: Spelling: 'ue'

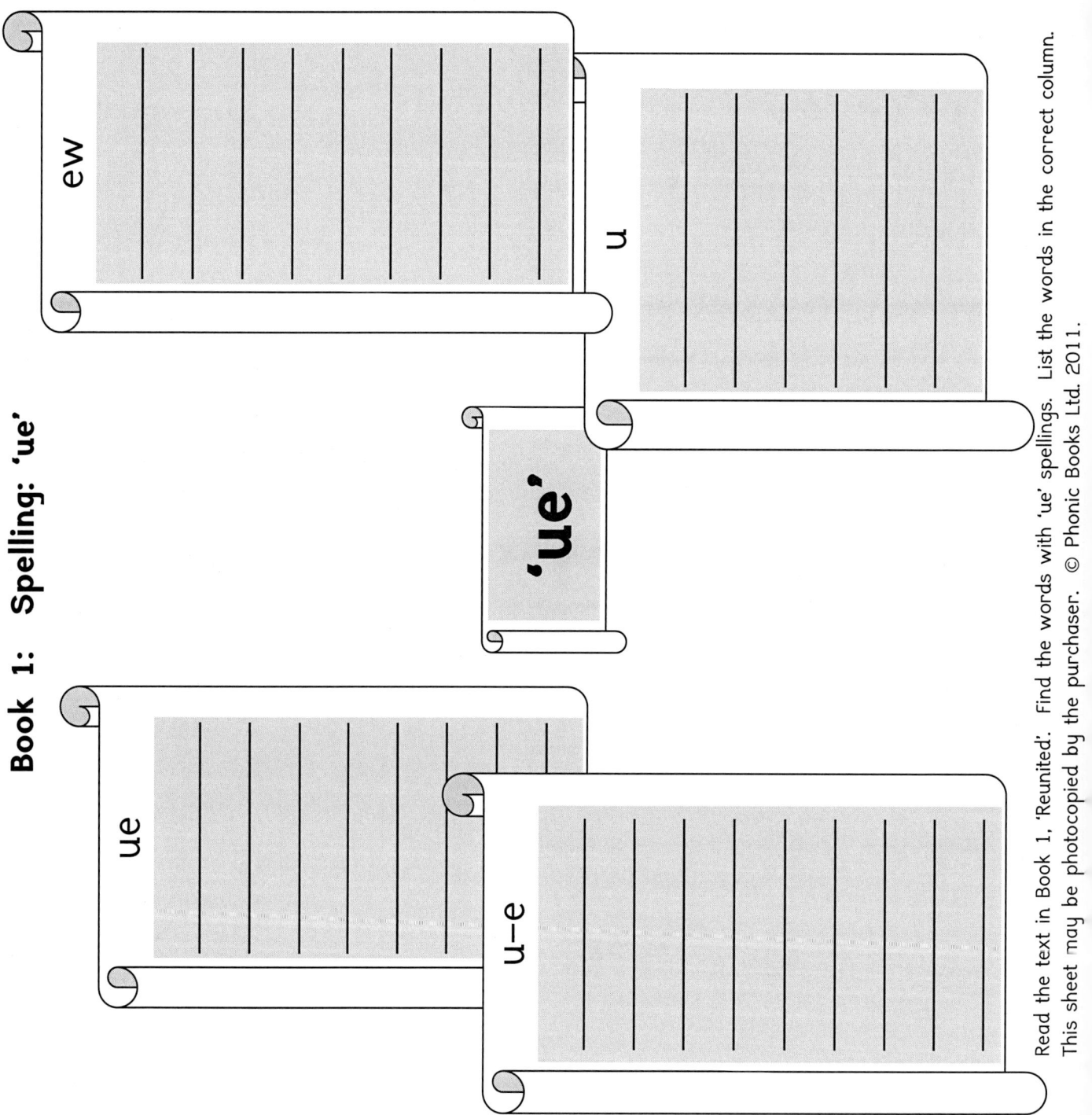

Read the text in Book 1, 'Reunited'. Find the words with 'ue' spellings. List the words in the correct column. This sheet may be photocopied by the purchaser. © Phonic Books Ltd. 2011.

Book 1: Reading and spelling

Grandpa rescued a puny mule from a bad man. He looked starved and abused. He was glad to have a new home. Mim scrubbed him down and gave him some food. The mule consumed it greedily.

Book 1: Is it true?

How many untruths can you spot in the text?

Zak did not want to resume the quest because he thought the talisman was useless. It had no new powers so he knew he would not be able to defeat the Dark Master. Grandpa said he should resume the quest to rescue all the animals in the world. Zak threw the talisman and it broke. Then it started to fuse into a brand new talisman.

Zak set off with a puny mule. When he stopped to rest, he hung the talisman on the mule because it was heavy. He woke up and the talisman had gone! Zak felt a bit stupid. He accused the mule and pushed him into a trap. The talisman saved the mule and changed him into a lynx.

How many untruths did you find?

Read this text after reading Book 1 'Reunited'. Underline the parts which are not true to the story in the book. Count the untruths and write the number in the box. This sheet may be photocopied by the purchaser. © Phonic Books Ltd. 2011.

Book 1: Writing

The mule – what is he like?

What he looks like:
skinny
bony
lean
skeletal

His fur is:
rough
coarse
silky
covered in sores

How he moves:
he limps
he stumbles
he gallops
he prances

He looks:
exhausted
afraid
confused
relieved

Describe the mule:
_____
_____
_____
_____
_____
_____
_____

Describe the mule. You can use some of the words in the boxes. This sheet may be photocopied by the purchaser. © Phonic Books Ltd. 2011.

Book 1: Comprehension

The lynx – true or false?

me di um

A sia

Am er ic a

Can ad a

re sem bles

whis kers

sol it ar y

crev ice s

squirr els

en dan gered

I be ri an

crit ic all y

Eurasian Lynx

The lynx is a medium-sized wild cat. It can be found in parts of Europe, Asia, America and Canada.

It has a short tail and tufts of black hair on the tips of its ears. It has a ruff under its neck which resembles a 'bow tie'. It has large padded paws for walking on snow and long whiskers on its face.

The lynx is a solitary animal. It lives in a den in crevices or ledges. A mother lynx may have one or two kittens. When they are nine months old, they move out of the den to live as young adults.

The lynx is a good climber and swimmer. It can swim fast and catch fish. It also hunts deer, hares, foxes, sheep, squirrels, mice, birds and goats.

There are four different kinds of lynx. The Canadian lynx is endangered. The Iberian lynx, which is found in Spain, is critically endangered.

Is it true?	yes	no
The lynx is a little cat.	☐	☐
It can be found in parts of Europe.	☐	☐
It has black tufts of hair on its ears.	☐	☐
Lynxes live and hunt in groups.	☐	☐
A ten-month old lynx will hunt with its mother.	☐	☐
The Iberian lynx in Spain may become extinct.	☐	☐

Read the text. Some multisyllable words are split for the reader. Now read the sentences below and tick the boxes according to whether they are true or false. This sheet may be photocopied by the purchaser. © Phonic Books Ltd. 2011.

Book 1: Extension activity: The lynx

Explain the following words:

solitary – _____

crevices – _____

critically endangered – _____

_____

The lynx is a solitary animal. Use a thesaurus to find two more words to describe someone who is 'solitary'.

1. _____   2. _____

Compare the lynx and the domestic cat.

What is the same about a lynx and a cat?

_____
_____
_____
_____
_____

What is the difference between a lynx and a cat?

_____
_____
_____
_____
_____

This extension activity follows on from the previous sheet 'True or False?'. This sheet may be photocopied by the purchaser. © Phonic Books Ltd. 2011.

Book 1: Splitting multisyllable words with 'ue' spellings 1a

use less	use	less	useless
mu sic			_____
res cue			_____
re fuse			_____
pu pil			_____
a ccuse			_____
stew ing			_____
sub due			_____
tune ful			_____
a mu sing			_____
rid ic ule			_____
att it ude			_____
fu ner al			_____
ab u sive			_____

Split the words into syllables. Sound out the syllables as you write them in the grey rectangles. Then write the whole word, saying the syllables as you do. This sheet may be photocopied by the purchaser.
© Phonic Books Ltd. 2011.

Book 1: Splitting multisyllable words with 'ue' spellings 1b

Word	Syllables			Whole word
useless	use	less		<u>useless</u>
music				_____
rescue				_____
refuse				_____
pupil				_____
accuse				_____
stewing				_____
subdue				_____
tuneful				_____
amusing				_____
ridicule				_____
attitude				_____
funeral				_____
abusive				_____

Split the words into syllables. Sound out the syllables as you write them in the grey rectangles. Then write the whole word, saying the syllables as you do. This sheet may be photocopied by the purchaser.
© Phonic Books Ltd. 2011.

Book 1: Stepping stones game: 'ue'

START → **FINISH**

- cute
- new
- due
- use
- few
- mule
- dew
- fuel
- rescue
- knew
- tune
- cue
- music
- duty
- abuse
- fuse
- stew
- tube
- refuse
- futile
- fume
- accuse
- pew
- amuse
- funeral
- hue
- useful
- news

This game is for 1–4 players. Play with counters and die. This sheet may be photocopied by the purchaser. © Phonic Books Ltd. 2011.

Book 2: Trouble in the Woods

Questions for discussion

Chapter 1

1. Why do you think Zak wants to call the mule Samson? (pg 1)

2. Why is Samson worried when he hears Mim wants to call him Tulip? (pg 2)

Chapter 2

1. Where is Volcano Island on the map? (pg 4)

Chapter 3

1. Why did Mim keep on tripping over? (pg 6)

2. Why did Zak and Mim start to quarrel? (pg 6)

Chapter 4

1. Why couldn't Mim breathe? (pg 8)

2. 'The beaver gnawed through the wood.' What does that mean? (pg 9)

Chapter 5

1. Why do you think Zak shape shifted into a beaver? (pg 11)

2. Why did Mim offer Zak some garlic? (pg 12)

3. How did Zak respond when Mim offered him garlic? (pg 12)

These questions can be discussed after reading the text. They are intended to develop speaking and listening skills and comprehension. This sheet may be photocopied by the purchaser. © Phonic Books Ltd. 2011.

Book 2: Blending and segmenting: 'o'

word					
hot	h	o	t		
want					
cough					
sausage					
what					
trough					
Austria					
squat					
wallet					
squash					
wander					
because					
swallow					

Blend the sounds into a word. Segment the word into sounds by writing one sound in each square. This sheet may be photocopied by the purchaser. © Phonic Books Ltd. 2011.

Book 2: Reading and sorting words with 'o' spellings

o	a	ou	au

dot	was	gone	want
cough	wash	squad	shone
wander	watch	prod	squabble
because	blog	quantity	swap
trough	swallow	drop	Austria
swat	wasp	font	wand
squalor	sausage	blond	qualify
wattle	wallow	squash	stomp

Photocopy this page onto card and cut out the words. Read and sort the cards out according to the 'o' headings at the top of the page. This sheet may be photocopied by the purchaser. © Phonic Books Ltd. 2011.

Book 2: Spelling 'o'

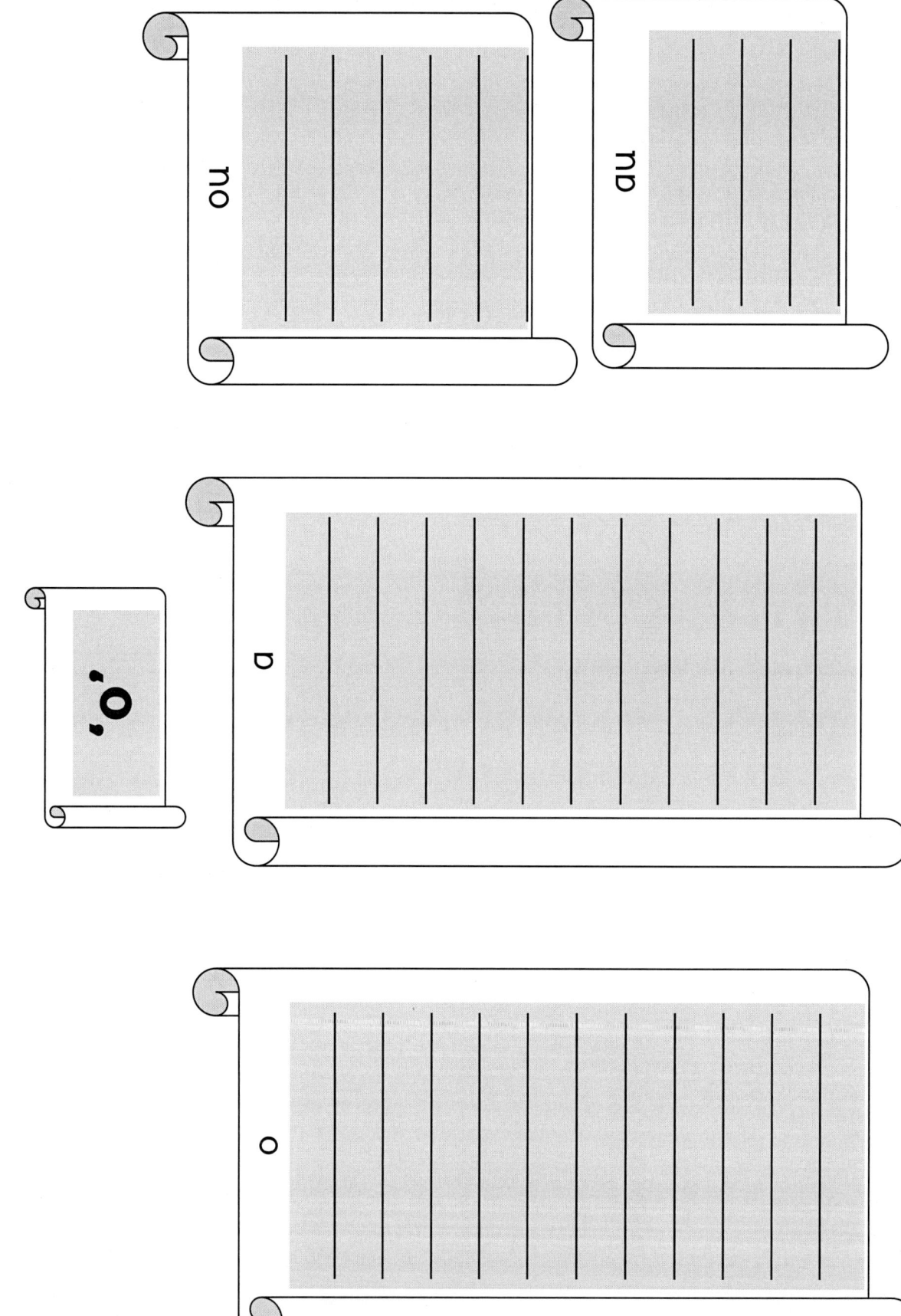

Read the text in Book 2, 'Trouble in the Woods'. Find the words with 'o' spellings. List the words in the correct column. © Phonic Books Ltd. 2011.
This sheet may be photocopied by the purchaser.

Book 2: Blending and segmenting: 'u'

word					
cup	c	u	p		
son					
touch					
bulb					
won					
young					
some					
money					
trouble					
dozen					
cousin					
above					
enough					

Blend the sounds into a word. Segment the word into sounds by writing one sound in each square.
This sheet may be photocopied by the purchaser. © Phonic Books Ltd. 2011.

Book 2: Reading and sorting words with 'u' spellings

u	ou	o

gut	some	touch	enough
cousin	ton	stun	money
swum	worry	come	couple
mother	nourish	glug	above
lush	young	brother	tough
son	rough	front	dozen
bunk	southern	nothing	courage
other	double	thump	another

Photocopy this page onto card and cut out the words. Read and sort the cards out according to the 'u' headings at the top of the page. This sheet may be photocopied by the purchaser. © Phonic Books Ltd. 2011.

Book 2: Spelling: 'u'

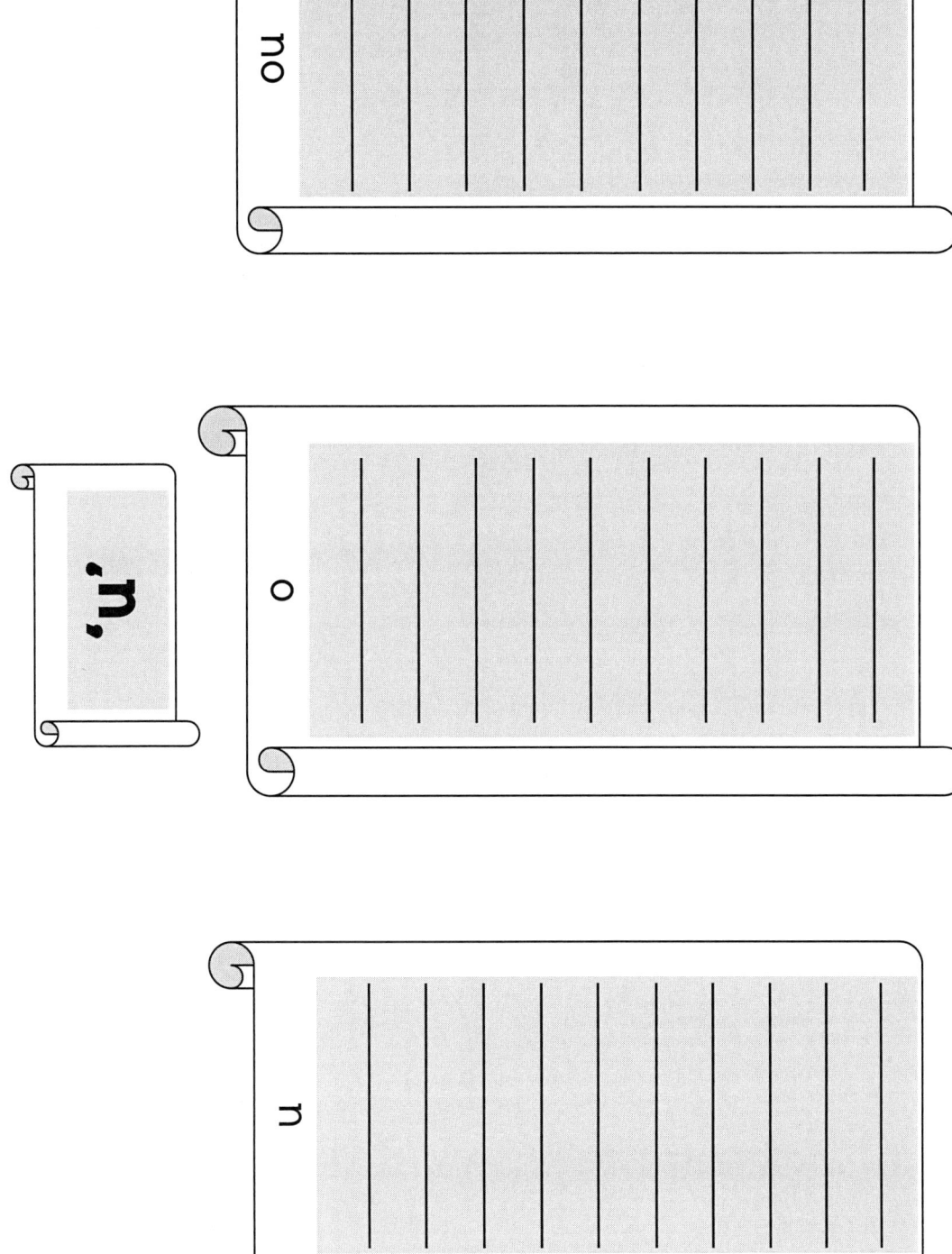

Read the text in Book 2, 'Trouble in the Woods'. Find the words with 'u' spellings. List the words in the correct column. © Phonic Books Ltd. 2011. This sheet may be photocopied by the purchaser.

Book 2: Reading and sorting words with <ou> spelling

you	touch	out

group	rough	about	route
pound	soup	young	wound
coupon	enough	mouse	courage
cloud	trouble	ghoul	hound
cousin	southern	count	house
double	tough	noun	found
ground	country	ounce	nourish

Photocopy this page onto card and cut out the words. Read and sort the cards out according to sounds of the <ou> spelling. The three sounds are: 'oo', 'u' and 'ow'. This sheet can also be used as a timed reading exercise. This sheet may be photocopied by the purchaser. © Phonic books Ltd. 2011.

Book 2: Reading and spelling

Mim was in trouble. The roots covered her body. Some of the roots were choking her. She began to cough. Zak watched in horror but he was in trouble too. The roots dragged him along the rough ground.

M _ _ _ _ _ in _ _ _ _ _ _.
The _ _ _ _ _ _ _ _ _ her _ _ _ _. _ _ _ of the _ _ _ _ were _ _ _ _ _ _ _. She _ _ _ _ _ to _ _ _ _. Zak _ _ _ _ _ _ _ _ _ _ _ _ but _ _ _ _ _ in _ _ _ _ _ _ too. The _ _ _ _ _ _ _ _ _ him _ _ _ _ the _ _ _ _ _ _ _ _ _ _.

Copy the text in the top scroll to the bottom scroll. Write a sound on each line e.g.: r ou gh. This activity can also be used for dictation. This sheet may be photocopied by the purchaser.
© Phonic Books Ltd. 2011.

Book 2: Is it true?

How many untruths can you spot in the text?

Mim and Zak wandered into the woods. They wondered what to call the mule. Zak said 'Samson' and Mim said 'Tulip'. They had a quarrel. Mim won and they agreed to call him 'Tulip'. Then Mim tripped over a root. She fell on the rough ground. A couple of roots began to twist around her arm. Soon she was pinned to the tree. She started to cough because she could not breathe. Zak was in trouble too because he was stung by a wasp. Then he shape shifted into a beaver. The beaver gnawed at the tree monster until it keeled over.

How many untruths did you find? ☐

Read this text after reading Book 2 'Trouble in the Woods'. Underline the parts which are not true to the story in the book. Count the untruths and write the number in the box. This sheet may be photocopied by the purchaser. © Phonic Books Ltd. 2011.

Book 2: Writing

The tree monster – what is it like?

What is it like?
scary
frightening
terrifying
creepy

Its eyes are like:
glowing coals
burning flames
sparkling jewels
evil snake's eyes

Its roots are like:
grabbing hands
twisting vines
choking strings
strangling fingers

It moves like:
an octopus
a thousand snakes
a ghost
a giant anaconda

Describe the tree monster:

_____
_____
_____
_____
_____
_____
_____

Describe the tree monster. You can use some of the words in the boxes. This sheet may be photocopied by the purchaser. © Phonic Books Ltd. 2011.

Book 2: Comprehension

The beaver – true or false?

ro dent	
spe cies	
Eu ra sian	
fa mous	
cre ate	
en tran ces	
pred a tors	
year lings	
noc tur nal	
sig nal	
dan ger	
mat er i als	

A beaver

The beaver is the second largest rodent in the world. There are two species: the North American and the Eurasian beaver.

Beavers are famous for the dams they build in rivers and streams. These dams create still ponds where they build their dens called 'lodges'.

The lodges have entrances only from the water so that predators cannot get inside. A lodge may have a pair of beavers and ten more family members inside. The babies are called 'yearlings'. Beavers mate for life. The older, two-year-old yearlings will look after the babies while the parents build the dams and stock up food.

Beavers are nocturnal, with poor eyesight but good senses of smell and touch. When they are alarmed, they slap their tails on the water to signal danger to other beavers.

Beavers are hard workers, always building dams or finding food and building materials. For this reason, 'to beaver' means to work hard.

Is it true?	yes	no
The beaver is the largest rodent in the world.	☐	☐
It builds dams to make ponds in rivers and streams.	☐	☐
Beavers' homes are called 'lodges'.	☐	☐
Beavers build dams in the daytime.	☐	☐
The male and female beavers stay together all their lives.	☐	☐
Beavers are lazy animals.	☐	☐

Read the text. Some multisyllable words are split for the reader. Now read the sentences below and tick the boxes according to whether they are true or false. This sheet may be photocopied by the purchaser. © Phonic Books Ltd. 2011.

Book 2: Extension activity: Beavers

Can you answer these questions?

1. What is a beaver lodge?

   _____
   _____
   _____

2. The beaver is a rodent. Which other animals are rodents?

   _____
   _____
   _____

3. The beaver is nocturnal. What does that mean?

   _____
   _____
   _____

4. How does a beaver warn other beavers when there is danger?

   _____
   _____
   _____

To 'beaver away' means to be busy and working hard because the beaver is a hard worker. Use a thesaurus to find two more words which mean 'busy'.

1. _____   2. _____

Book 2: Splitting multisyllable words with 'o' spellings 1a

dropp ing	▭ ▭		dropping
wa llet	▭ ▭		_____
be cause	▭ ▭		_____
cough ing	▭ ▭		_____
squabb le	▭ ▭		_____
swa llowed	▭ ▭		_____
squad ron	▭ ▭		_____
watch ful	▭ ▭		_____
saus age	▭ ▭		_____
quan tit y	▭ ▭ ▭		_____
un wan ted	▭ ▭ ▭		_____
qua lit y	▭ ▭ ▭		_____
wan der ing	▭ ▭ ▭		_____
qua lif ied	▭ ▭ ▭		_____

Split the words into syllables. Sound out the syllables as you write them in the grey rectangles. Then write the whole word, saying the syllables as you do. This sheet may be photocopied by the purchaser. © Phonic Books Ltd. 2011.

Book 2: Splitting multisyllable words with 'o' spellings 1b

dropping <u>dropping</u>

wallet _____

because _____

coughing _____

squabble _____

swallowed _____

squadron _____

watchful _____

sausage _____

quantity _____

unwanted _____

quality _____

wandering _____

qualified _____

Split the words into syllables. Sound out the syllables as you write them in the grey rectangles. Then write the whole word, saying the syllables as you do. This sheet may be photocopied by the purchaser. © Phonic Books Ltd. 2011.

Book 2: Splitting multisyllable words with 'u' spellings 1a

thump ing	thump	ing	<u>thumping</u>
cou sin			_____
mon key			_____
do zen			_____
e nough			_____
bro ther			_____
south ern			_____
no thing			_____
nou rish ing			_____
mo ther ly			_____
wo rry ing			_____
a no ther			_____
won der ing			_____
gov ern ment			_____

Split the words into syllables. Sound out the syllables as you write them in the grey rectangles. Then write the whole word, saying the syllables as you do. This sheet may be photocopied by the purchaser. © Phonic Books Ltd. 2011.

Book 2: Splitting multisyllable words with 'u' spellings 1b

word	syllable 1	syllable 2	syllable 3	whole word
thumping	thump	ing		<u>thumping</u>
cousin				_____
monkey				_____
dozen				_____
enough				_____
brother				_____
southern				_____
nothing				_____
nourishing				_____
motherly				_____
worrying				_____
another				_____
wondering				_____
government				_____

Split the words into syllables. Sound out the syllables as you write them in the grey rectangles. Then write the whole word, saying the syllables as you do. This sheet may be photocopied by the purchaser. © Phonic Books Ltd. 2011.

Book 2: Stepping stones game: 'u' and 'o'

START → **FINISH**

- snug
- cousin
- worry
- plot
- want
- squash
- front
- other
- dozen
- swat
- tough
- cough
- above
- wasp
- because
- couple
- son
- wallet
- sausage
- nothing
- enough
- quantity
- young
- swallow
- double
- nourish
- rough
- swap

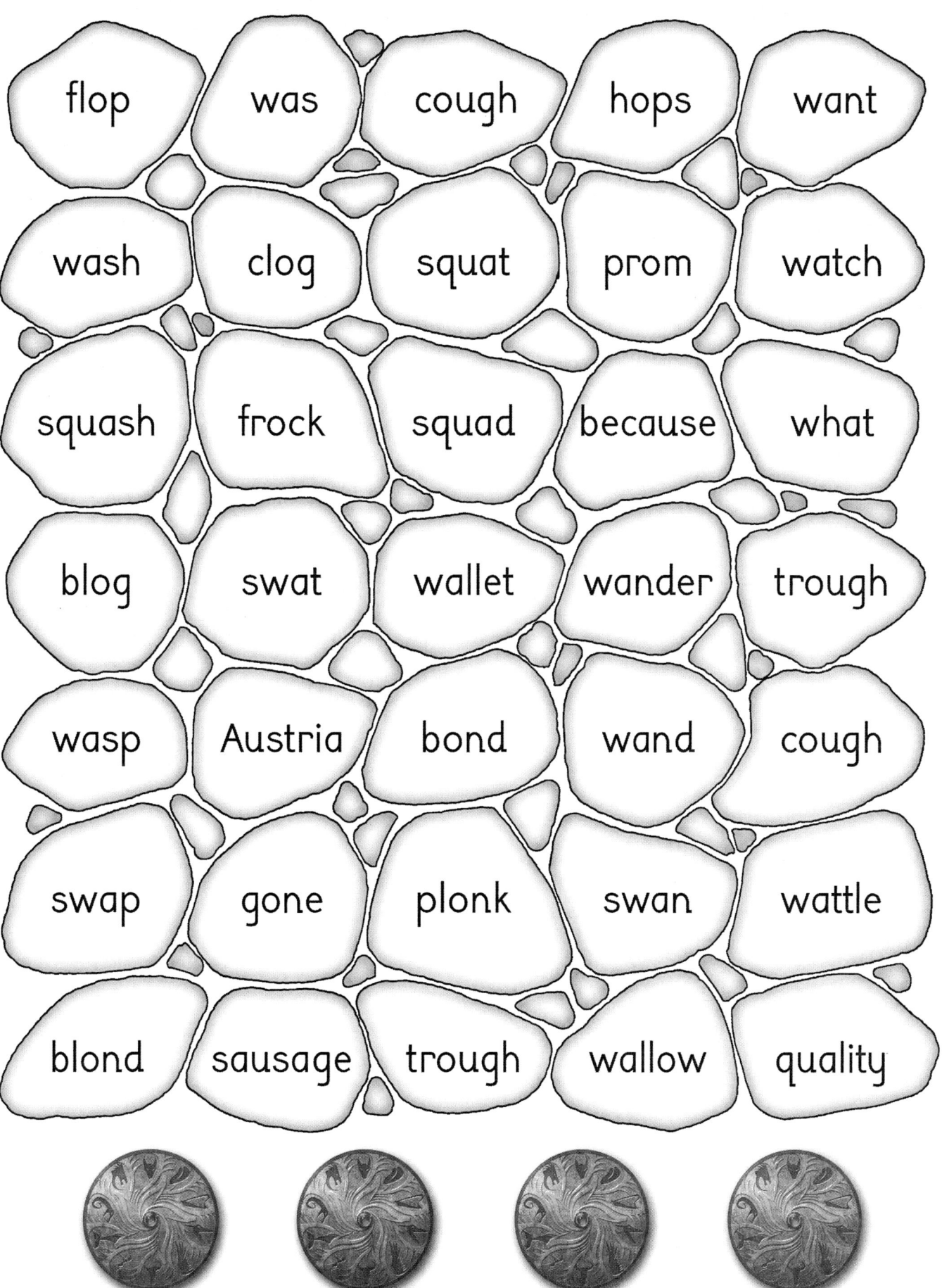

Book 2: 4-in-a-row game: 'u'

but	tough	young	come	plug
cousin	son	love	double	uncle
trouble	nothing	ton	rubbish	mother
brother	trumps	above	cover	nourish
enough	touch	rough	blunt	oven
dozen	rumble	money	other	couple
fluff	worry	glove	London	among

Play with two sets of coloured counters. Two players take turns to read the word and put a counter on the word. The winner is the first to get four of his or her counters in a row. The winner places a counter on a talisman. The game is played four times until all the talismans are covered. This sheet may be photocopied by the purchaser.
© Phonic Books Ltd. 2011.

Book 3: Certain Death

Questions for discussion

Chapter 1

1. Mim and Zak walked into a dense forest. What is a dense forest? (pg 1)
2. Why did Mim pick wild lettuce in the forest? (pg 2)

Chapter 2

1. 'The sun descended into a golden horizon.' What is this sentence describing? (pg 4)

Chapter 3

1. Why do you think they fell into a trance? (pg 6)
2. What did Mim and Zak see in the three pairs of eyes? (pgs 6 and 7)

Chapter 4

1. How did Samson save the day? (pg 8)
2. Why didn't the cakes pacify Cerberus? (pg 9)

Chapter 5

1. How did Mim get Cerberus to sleep? (pg 10)
2. Why did Samson fall asleep too? (pg 11)

These questions can be discussed after reading the text. They are intended to develop speaking and listening skills and comprehension. This sheet may be photocopied by the purchaser. © Phonic Books Ltd. 2011.

Book 3: Blending and segmenting: 's'

sand	s	a	n	d	
mess					
rinse					
cell					
fence					
muscle					
listen					
gloss					
house					
cinema					
dance					
scissors					
castle					

Blend the sounds into a word. Segment the word into sounds by writing one sound in each square.
This sheet may be photocopied by the purchaser. © Phonic Books Ltd. 2011.

Book 3: Reading and sorting words with 's' spellings

s	ss	se	c

ce	sc	st

spent	press	rinse	cent
cellar	tense	slot	wince
swum	fence	scene	castle
cement	voice	horse	science
scent	whistle	sing	century
circle	listen	scissors	muscle
certain	distress	worse	descend
balance	race	peace	cycle

Photocopy this page onto card and cut out the words. Read and sort the cards out according to the 's' headings at the top of the page. This sheet may be photocopied by the purchaser. © Phonic Books Ltd. 2011.

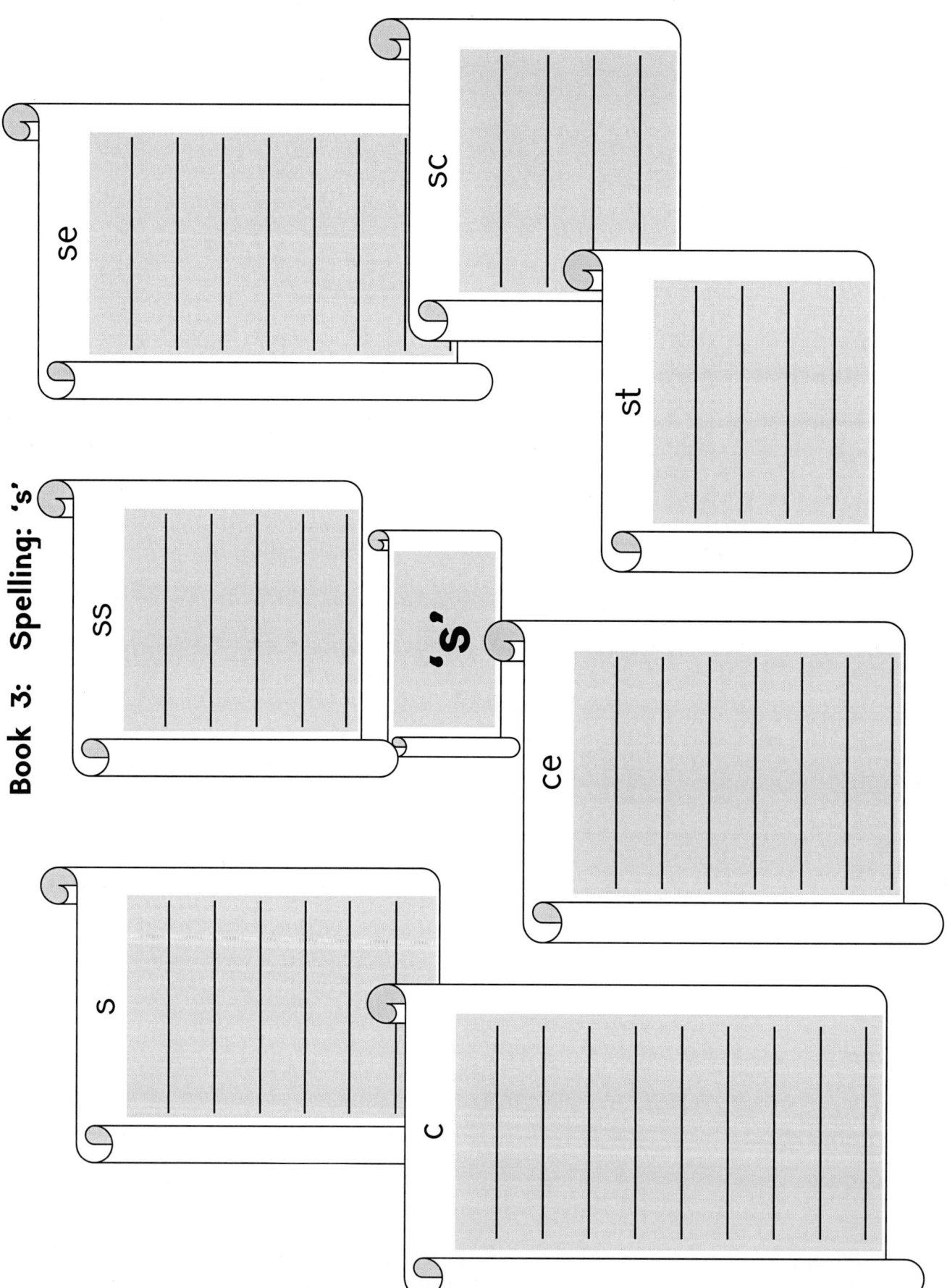

Book 3: Reading and sorting words with <c> spelling

| cat | cent |

crust	civil	clap	cycle
circle	centre	focus	certain
ceiling	care	cement	census
cloud	celebrate	cold	cell
crisp	cigar	uncle	century
castle	ceramic	celebrity	cedar

Photocopy this page onto card and cut out the words. Read and sort the cards out according to sounds of the <c> spelling. The two sounds are: 'k' and 's'. This sheet can also be used as a timed reading exercise. This sheet may be photocopied by the purchaser. © Phonic books Ltd. 2011.

Book 3: Reading and spelling

Zak listened for the rustle again. He was tense. He glanced about him. Was that a glimpse of a shadow? He was certain it was. The moon ascended into the purple sky. He smelled the scent of dog. It was Cerberus!

Zak _ _ _ _ _ for the _ _ _ _ _ _ _ _ _. He _ _ _ _ _ _ _. He _ _ _ _ _ _ _ _ _ him. _ _ _ _ _ _ a _ _ _ _ _ _ of a _ _ _ _ _? He was _ _ _ _ _ _ _ it _ _ _. The _ _ _ _ _ _ _ _ _ _ _ into the _ _ _ _ _ _ _ _ _. He _ _ _ _ _ _ the _ _ _ _ of _ _ _. It was _ _ _ _ _ _ _!

Copy the text in the top scroll to the bottom scroll. Write a sound on each line e.g.: sc e n t. This activity can also be used for dictation. This sheet may be photocopied by the purchaser.
© Phonic Books Ltd. 2011.

Book 3: Writing

Cerberus – what is it like?

What is it like?
dangerous
savage
ferocious
fierce

Its eyes are like:
glowing lamps
yellow jewels
blinding lights
shiny mirrors

Its teeth are as:
pointed as nails
sharp as razors
stinky as rotten meat
black as coals

It moves in a:
lunging way
jerky way
threatening way
aggressive way

Describe Cerberus:

_____

_____

_____

_____

_____

_____

_____

Describe Cerberus. You can use some of the words in the boxes. This sheet may be photocopied by the purchaser. © Phonic Books Ltd. 2011.

Book 3: Is it true?

How many untruths can you spot in the text?

Zak and Mim walked into a dense forest. Zak listened. He heard a rustle. He sensed that they were being watched. Mim was busy picking wild lettuce and took no notice. The sun descended as dusk came down and the moon ascended into the sky. Zak and Mim decided to have a nap. Suddenly, six yellow eyes danced about in the black night. It was Cerberus, the six-headed hound. They looked into the eyes and saw their past, their present and their future. Cerberus's muscles glistened, ready to attack. Mim threw three cakes at the hound. The cakes were magic cakes and Cerberus was pacified and collapsed into a deep sleep.

How many untruths did you find? ☐

Read this text after reading Book 3, 'Certain Death'. Underline the parts which are not true to the story in the book. Count the untruths and write the number in the box. This sheet may be photocopied by the purchaser. © Phonic Books Ltd. 2011.

Book 3: Comprehension

Cerberus – true or false?

Cer ber us

myth o lo gy

un der world

Cerberus is a multi-headed hound in Greek and Roman mythology. His job was to guard Hades, the underworld. He allowed the spirits of the dead to enter the underworld but not to leave.

In some places, Cerberus is shown with one, two, three or up to fifty heads.

Cerberus

de pict

Most sources depict Cerberus with three heads. Some say the three heads represented the past, present and the future. Others say they represented birth, youth and old age.

rep re sent ed

Her ac les

man aged

The most famous story of Cerberus in Greek mythology tells how Heracles had to capture him with his bare hands. Heracles managed to slip into Hades and to overcome Cerberus. He slung him over his shoulder and brought him back to the land of the living. But Cerberus was so fierce that Heracles had to quickly return the hound to Hades.

Cerberus has appeared in many modern fantasy stories.

fan tas y

Is it true?	yes	no
Cerberus always has three heads.	☐	☐
Cerberus comes from Greek and Roman mythology.	☐	☐
Cerberus is the guard of heaven.	☐	☐
Cerberus allowed the spirits of the dead in and out.	☐	☐
Heracles carried Cerberus on his shoulder.	☐	☐
Modern authors do not like to write about Cerberus.	☐	☐

Read the text. Some multisyllable words are split for the reader. Now read the sentences below and tick the boxes according to whether they are true or false. This sheet may be photocopied by the purchaser. © Phonic Books Ltd. 2011.

Book 3: Extension activity: Cerberus

Explain the following words:

to depict – _____

a source – _____

fierce – _____

Cerberus was a fierce hound. Use a thesaurus to find two more words that describe the word 'fierce'.

1. _____ 2. _____

Here is another creature with more than one head. It is a Chimera. Describe it.

_____
_____
_____
_____
_____
_____

This extension activity follows on from the previous sheet 'True or False?'. This sheet may be photocopied by the purchaser. © Phonic Books Ltd. 2011.

Book 3: Splitting multisyllable words with 's' spellings 1a

stand ing   ☐ ☐   <u>standing</u>

mess y   ☐ ☐   _____

non sense   ☐ ☐   _____

list en   ☐ ☐   _____

cem ent   ☐ ☐   _____

de cide   ☐ ☐   _____

imm ense   ☐ ☐   _____

sci ence   ☐ ☐   _____

de cim al   ☐ ☐ ☐   _____

cel eb rate   ☐ ☐ ☐   _____

mist le toe   ☐ ☐ ☐   _____

disc ip line   ☐ ☐ ☐   _____

fasc i nate   ☐ ☐ ☐   _____

ac ci dent   ☐ ☐ ☐   _____

Split the words into syllables. Sound out the syllables as you write them in the grey rectangles. Then write the whole word, saying the syllables as you do. This sheet may be photocopied by the purchaser. © Phonic Books Ltd. 2011.

Book 3: Splitting multisyllable words with 's' spellings 1b

standing standing

messy _____

nonsense _____

listen _____

cement _____

decide _____

immense _____

science _____

decimal _____

celebrate _____

mistletoe _____

discipline _____

fascinate _____

accident _____

Split the words into syllables. Sound out the syllables as you write them in the grey rectangles. Then write the whole word, saying the syllables as you do. This sheet may be photocopied by the purchaser. © Phonic Books Ltd. 2011.

Book 3: Homophones 1: which is which?

cell	sell		cent	scent

seen	scene		muscles	mussels

piece	peace		place	plaice

site	sight		seller	cellar

The student can draw an image on each card to help him/her remember the meaning of the word. Photocopy the cards and play pelmanism. This sheet may be photocopied by the purchaser.
© Phonic Books Ltd. 2011.

Book 3: Homophones 2: cell or sell?

1. I can _____ my boots for £20.00.
2. The prisoner was locked up in a _____.
3. I paid one dollar and forty _____ s for that badge.
4. The roses had a lovely _____.
5. The best _____ in the movie was at the end.
6. Have you _____ my school bag? I can't find it.
7. I lift weights to build up my _____.
8. The French like to eat _____ with chips.
9. The homeless man found a _____ to stay.
10. A _____ is a flat fish you can eat.
11. There was a tall crane on the building _____.
12. The blind man lost his eye _____.
13. The rich man kept his wine in his _____.
14. The fruit _____ had a stall at the market.
15. The people prayed for _____.
16. Ben helped himself to a large _____ of cake.

cell   sell   scent   cent   muscles   mussels   piece   peace

plaice   place   seen   scene   seller   cellar   site   sight

Read the sentences above. The student can use the homophone cards from the previous page to select the correct homophone for each sentence. This sheet may be photocopied by the purchaser. © Phonic Books Ltd. 2011.

Book 3: Stepping stones game: 's'

START

FINISH

- still
- cycle
- loss
- fence
- since
- house
- bliss
- wince
- dance
- rinse
- muscle
- whistle
- fasten
- bossy
- cellar
- cent
- central
- cyber
- listen
- science
- trance
- horse
- worse
- scene
- thistle
- certain
- necessary
- descend

This game is for 1–4 players. Play with counters and die. This sheet may be photocopied by the purchaser. © Phonic Books Ltd. 2011.

Book 3: 4-in-a-row game: 's'

spin	fuss	cell	nice	house
circle	force	scissors	certain	rinse
prance	tense	cycle	science	listen
castle	scent	wince	cent	chase
race	cigar	cyber	goose	whistle
scene	worse	centre	slice	ascend
hustle	citizen	notice	horse	city

Play with two sets of coloured counters. Two players take turns to read the word and put a counter on the word. The winner is the first to get four of his or her counters in a row. The winner places a counter on a talisman. The game is played four times until all the talismans are covered. This sheet may be photocopied by the purchaser.
© Phonic Books Ltd. 2011.

Book 4: The Fossil

Questions for discussion

Chapter 1

1. Why was Zak unhappy camping near the gravel quarry? (pg 1)

2. What does the word 'frugal' mean? (pg 2)

3. How are the stars described on page 2? (pg 2)

Chapter 2

1. What happened to Samson? (pg 4)

2. 'They ran to the edge of the gravel quarry and peered over.' What does that mean? (pg 4)

3. Why does Mim say, "Typical, just typical!"? (pg 5)

Chapter 3

1. How does the fossil come to life? (pg 7)

Chapter 4

1. Why couldn't Zak escape from the quarry? (pg 8)

Chapter 5

1. What do you think people would say when they hear Zak's story about the fossil bug? (pg 12)

These questions can be discussed after reading the text. They are intended to develop speaking and listening skills and comprehension. This sheet may be photocopied by the purchaser. © Phonic Books Ltd. 2011.

Book 4: Blending and segmenting: 'l'

lamp	l	a	m	p
smell				
middle				
final				
pupil				
camel				
idol				
drill				
simple					
signal					
pencil					
mental					
travel					

Blend the sounds into a word. Segment the word into sounds by writing one sound in each square. This sheet may be photocopied by the purchaser. © Phonic Books Ltd. 2011.

Book 4: Reading and sorting words with 'l' spellings

| l | ll | le | al |

| il | el | ol |

long	thrill	gabble	animal
camel	metal	pencil	gamble
April	bottle	cancel	channel
medal	peril	pimple	pistol
silly	panel	mammal	evil
grumble	critical	petrol	fuel
travel	pupil	final	idol
signal	poodle	suckle	tunnel

Photocopy this page onto card and cut out the words. Read and sort the cards out according to the 'l' headings at the top of the page. This sheet may be photocopied by the purchaser. © Phonic Books Ltd. 2011.

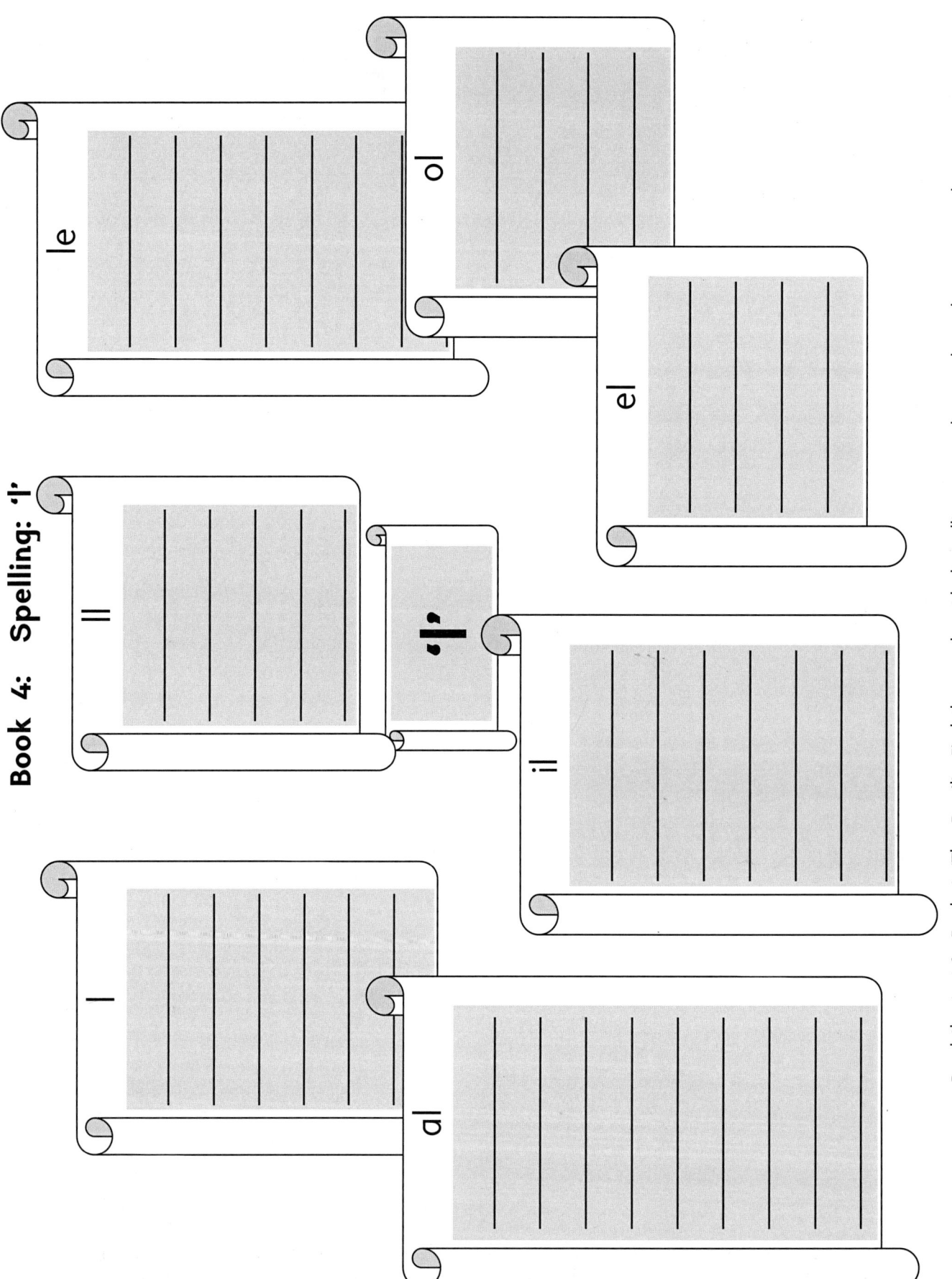

Book 4: Reading and spelling

Zak dug the fossil out of the rock. An evil-looking bug fell out onto the gravel. It looked brutal. It began to scuttle towards him. Zak thought his life was in peril but he was trapped in the quarry.

Copy the text in the top scroll to the bottom scroll. Write a sound on each line e.g.: f o ss il. Where the vowel spelling is split (i–e), there is a link e.g.: l i f e . This activity can also be used for dictation. This sheet may be photocopied by the purchaser. © Phonic Books Ltd. 2011.

Book 4: Is it true?

How many untruths can you spot in the text?

Mim and Zak travelled on until they reached a gravel quarry. They camped by the quarry and ate a frugal meal of bread and jam. The next day, Samson sniffed some grass with his nostrils. He nibbled the grass by the edge of the quarry and fell over the edge. Then the talisman tumbled down too. Zak went down into the quarry to rescue Samson. He spotted a fossil. The fossil glowed and fell out of the rock. It was made of metal. Zak's life was in peril when the fossil attacked. Zak shape shifted into a pteranodon. He lifted Samson and flew off with him. Zak kept a fossil to take back to the village.

How many untruths did you find?

Read this text after reading Book 4, 'The Fossil'. Underline the parts which are not true to the story in the book. Count the untruths and write the number in the box. This sheet may be photocopied by the purchaser. © Phonic Books Ltd. 2011.

Book 4: Writing

The fossil bug – what is it like?

It is shiny like:
a polished shoe
a black pebble
black mirrors

Its pincers are:
like thorns
like crab claws
like spears
like crushing teeth

Its legs are:
creepy
scary
alarming
chilling

It moves like this:
it scuttles
it darts
it creeps
it charges

Describe the fossil bug:

_____
_____
_____
_____
_____
_____
_____

Describe the fossil bug. You can use some of the words in the boxes. This sheet may be photocopied by the purchaser. © Phonic Books Ltd. 2011.

Book 4: Comprehension

Pteranodon – true or false?

pter an od on

di no saurs

pter o saurs

Pteranodon

In books and films, pteranodon are often shown as dinosaurs but they are not dinosaurs. They are pterosaurs. This is a group of flying reptiles that lived on earth between 220 and 65 million years ago.

There are over 1,000 fossils of both female and male pteranodon so a great deal is known about them.

av er age

wing span

ex ten ed

sci en tists

The average wingspan of a male pteranodon was 5.6 metres. The average wingspan of a female was 3.8 metres. The wings were made of skin and muscle that stretched from the legs to an extended finger. Pteranodon had toothless beaks, similar to bird beaks. They had a bony crest on their skulls.

stom achs

sugg est

Scientists have found fossil bones of fish in the stomachs of pteranodon, which suggests that they ate fish. It is now thought that they could swim and take off from the water.

Pteranodon fossils have been found in North America.

Is it true?	yes	no
Pteranodon are dinosaurs.	☐	☐
Pteranodon are extinct.	☐	☐
Females were larger than males.	☐	☐
Pteranodon had teeth.	☐	☐
They were vegetarian.	☐	☐
Pteranodon skeletons were found around the world.	☐	☐

Read the text. Some multisyllable words are split for the reader. Now read the sentences below and tick the boxes according to whether they are true or false. This sheet may be photocopied by the purchaser. © Phonic Books Ltd. 2011.

Book 4: Extension activity: Fill in the missing words

Fill in the missing words so that the text makes sense.

Pteranodon

In books and films, pteranodon are often shown as _____ but they are not dinosaurs – they are pterosaurs. This is a group of reptiles that could _____. They lived on earth between 220 and 65 million _____ ago.

There are over 1,000 fossils of both female and _____ pteranodon so a great deal is known about them.

The average wingspan _____ a male pteranodon was 5.6 metres. The average wingspan of a _____ was 3.8 metres. The wings were made of skin and muscle that stretched from the legs to an extended _____. Pteranodon had toothless beaks, similar to _____ beaks. They had a bony crest on their skulls.

Scientists have found fossil bones of _____ in the stomachs of pteranodon, which suggests that they _____ fish. It is now thought that they could swim and take off _____ the water.

Pteranodon fossils have been _____ in North America.

Book 4: Splitting multisyllable words with 'l' spellings 1a

Syllables		Whole word
limp ing	▭ ▭	<u>limping</u>
un well	▭ ▭	_____
shutt le	▭ ▭	_____
cam el	▭ ▭	_____
e vil	▭ ▭	_____
i dol	▭ ▭	_____
sig nal	▭ ▭	_____
stum ble	▭ ▭	_____
an im al	▭ ▭ ▭	_____
i dle ness	▭ ▭ ▭	_____
crit ic al	▭ ▭ ▭	_____
un scram ble	▭ ▭ ▭	_____
ca pa ble	▭ ▭ ▭	_____
in ter val	▭ ▭ ▭	_____

Split the words into syllables. Sound out the syllables as you write them in the grey rectangles. Then write the whole word, saying the syllables as you do. This sheet may be photocopied by the purchaser. © Phonic Books Ltd. 2011.

Book 4: Splitting multisyllable words with 'l' spellings 1b

limping	☐ ☐	<u>limping</u>
unwell	☐ ☐	_____
shuttle	☐ ☐	_____
camel	☐ ☐	_____
evil	☐ ☐	_____
idol	☐ ☐	_____
signal	☐ ☐	_____
stumble	☐ ☐	_____
animal	☐ ☐ ☐	_____
idleness	☐ ☐ ☐	_____
critical	☐ ☐ ☐	_____
unscramble	☐ ☐ ☐	_____
capable	☐ ☐ ☐	_____
interval	☐ ☐ ☐	_____

Split the words into syllables. Sound out the syllables as you write them in the grey rectangles. Then write the whole word, saying the syllables as you do. This sheet may be photocopied by the purchaser. © Phonic Books Ltd. 2011.

Book 4: Stepping stones game: 'l'

START → **FINISH**

- able
- spill
- length
- model
- animal
- pupil
- dismal
- central
- evil
- capital
- idol
- giggle
- pencil
- principal
- camel
- hostel
- illegal
- steeple
- bridal
- peril
- stumble
- cancel
- petrol
- mammal
- final
- April
- metal
- pistol

Book 4: 4-in-a-row game: 'l'

lump	shell	muddle	metal	pupil
medal	dental	civil	idol	simple
evil	single	collect	tidal	dial
final	pollen	level	ramble	animal
signal	cancel	rival	thrills	pencil
crinkle	gravel	camel	shovel	peril
novel	kennel	April	shuttle	capital

Play with two sets of coloured counters. Two players take turns to read the word and put a counter on the word. The winner is the first to get four of his or her counters in a row. The winner places a counter on a talisman. The game is played four times until all the talismans are covered. This sheet may be photocopied by the purchaser.
© Phonic Books Ltd. 2011.

Book 5: Legends of the Gorge

Questions for discussion

Chapter 1

1. What is a gorge? (pg 1)

2. Why was Mim feeling 'fragile'? (pg 2)

Chapter 2

1. How did Zak fall over the edge? (pg 3)

2. When Mim asked Zak if he had any 'damage', what did she mean? (pg 4)

Chapter 3

1. Do you think Zak believed in the legend of the gorge when he told Mim about it? Explain. (pg 6)

2. Why does Mim say that the legend is "very original"? (pg 6)

Chapter 4

1. How does Mim coax Samson onto the bridge? (pg 8)

Chapter 5

1. Why won't Zak shape shift into an eagle? (pg 10)

2. What do you think Samson was thinking as he flew away with Zak and Mim on his back? (pg 12)

These questions can be discussed after reading the text. They are intended to develop speaking and listening skills and comprehension. This sheet may be photocopied by the purchaser. © Phonic Books Ltd. 2011.

Book 5: Blending and segmenting: 'j'

junk	j	u	n	k			
gem							
page							
edge							
adjust							
giant							
manage							
logic							
bridge							
legend							
cottage							
adjective							
badge							

Blend the sounds into a word. Segment the word into sounds by writing one sound in each square.
This sheet may be photocopied by the purchaser.   © Phonic Books Ltd. 2011.

Book 5: Reading and sorting words with 'j' spellings

| j | g | ge | dge | dj |

jest	gel	rage	edge
badge	adjust	giant	lodge
gentle	stage	hedge	grudge
fudge	village	just	germ
gist	adjective	sledge	jumper
dodge	joke	gem	manage
bridge	ginger	adjacent	pledge
tragedy	cottage	jelly	logic

Photocopy this page onto card and cut out the words. Read and sort the cards out according to the 'j' headings at the top of the page. This sheet may be photocopied by the purchaser. © Phonic Books Ltd. 2011.

Book 5: Spelling: 'j'

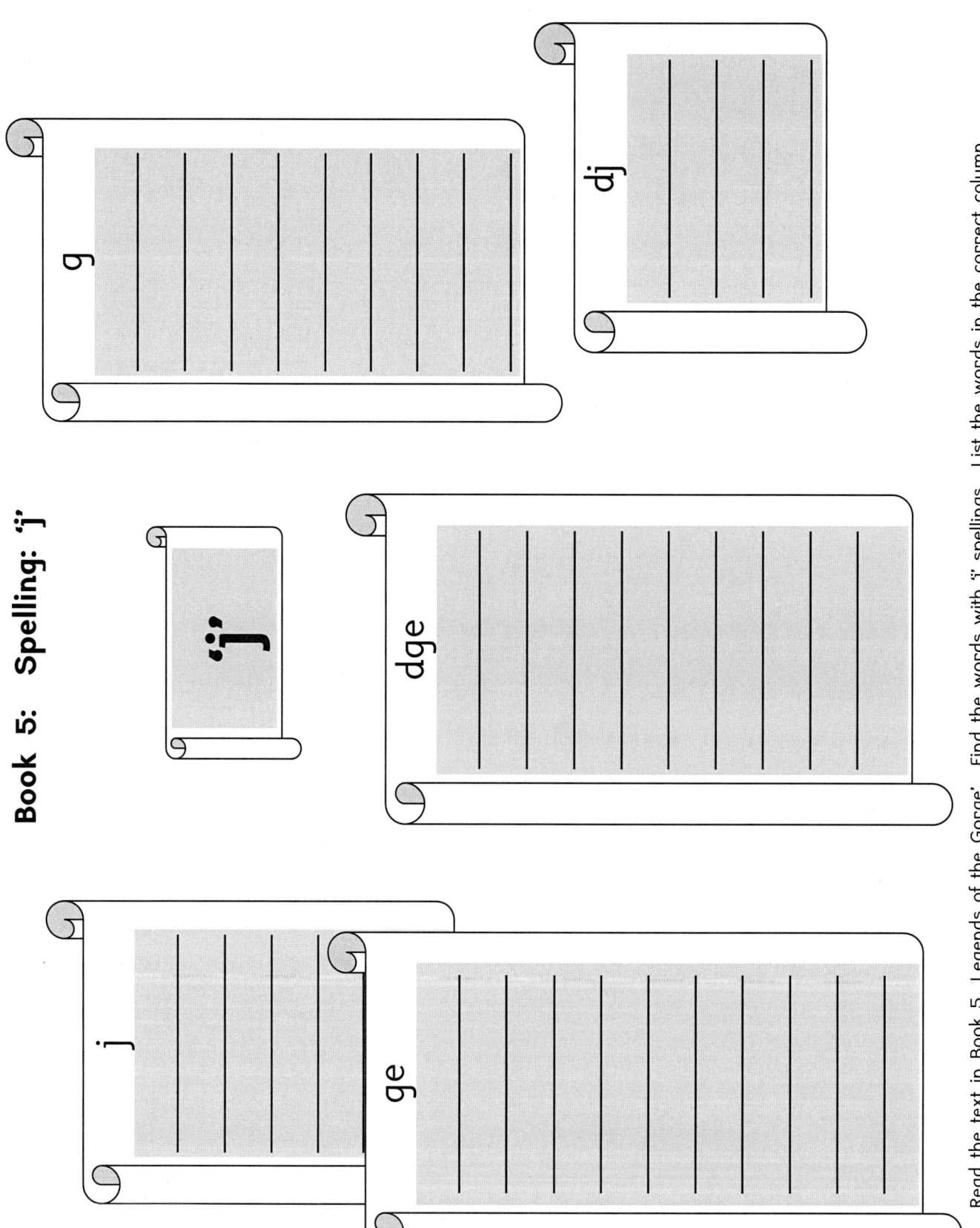

Read the text in Book 5, Legends of the Gorge'. Find the words with 'j' spellings. List the words in the correct column. This sheet may be photocopied by the purchaser. © Phonic Books Ltd. 2011.

Book 5: Reading and spelling

Mim did not believe the legend of the gorge. Just then, a giant hand shook the bridge. Mim surged forward and dragged Samson along the bridge. Zak watched in horror as the wooden slats plunged into the gorge.

Mim _ _ _   _ _ _
_ _ _ _ _ _   the   _ _ _ _ _
_ _   the   _ _ _.   _ _ _ _
_ _ _, a _ _ _ _ _   _ _ _ _
shook the   _ _ _ _.   Mim
_ _ _ _ _ _   _ _ _ _ _ _   and
_ _ _ _ _ _   _ _ _ _ _
_ _ _ _   the   _ _ _ _.   Zak
watched   _ _   _ _ _ _
as the   _ _ _ _ _ _ _ _
_ _ _ _ _ _   into the   _ _ _.

Copy the text in the top scroll to the bottom scroll. Write a sound on each line e.g.: g or ge. This activity can also be used for dictation. This sheet may be photocopied by the purchaser.
© Phonic Books Ltd. 2011.

Book 5: Reading and sorting words with <g> spelling

| gap | gem |

grit	gym	gulp	gel
girl	gate	giant	urgent
ginger	grand	germ	gust
gentle	giraffe	logic	glass
glue	biology	rigid	glance
flag	tragic	gabble	legend

Photocopy this page onto card and cut out the words. Read and sort the cards out according to sounds of the spelling <g>. The two sounds are: 'g' and 'j'. This sheet can also be used as a timed reading exercise. This sheet may be photocopied by the purchaser. © Phonic books Ltd. 2011.

Book 5: Is it true?

How many untruths can you spot in the text?

Mim and Zak trudged on until they came to a gorge. Mim felt her energy drain away because she was tired. Zak tried to cheer her up but ended up hanging from a ledge, rigid with fear. Mim managed to pull him up. Zak damaged his hand and Mim put a bandage on it. Then, they saw a bridge. It was made of rope and wood. Samson skipped across it. Suddenly, the bridge shook and a giant ogre appeared from below. Zak turned Samson into Pegasus, the flying horse. He looked magical! He had magnificent wings! Zak and Mim were so pleased with Samson that they gave him fudge to eat.

How many untruths did you find?

Read this text after reading Book 5, 'Legends of the Gorge'. Underline the parts which are not true to the story in the book. Count the untruths and write the number in the box. This sheet may be photocopied by the purchaser. © Phonic Books Ltd. 2011.

Book 5: Writing

The ogre – what is it like?

It is:
massive
enormous
gigantic
huge

Its teeth look:
like pegs
like tombstones
broken and missing
like slabs of stone

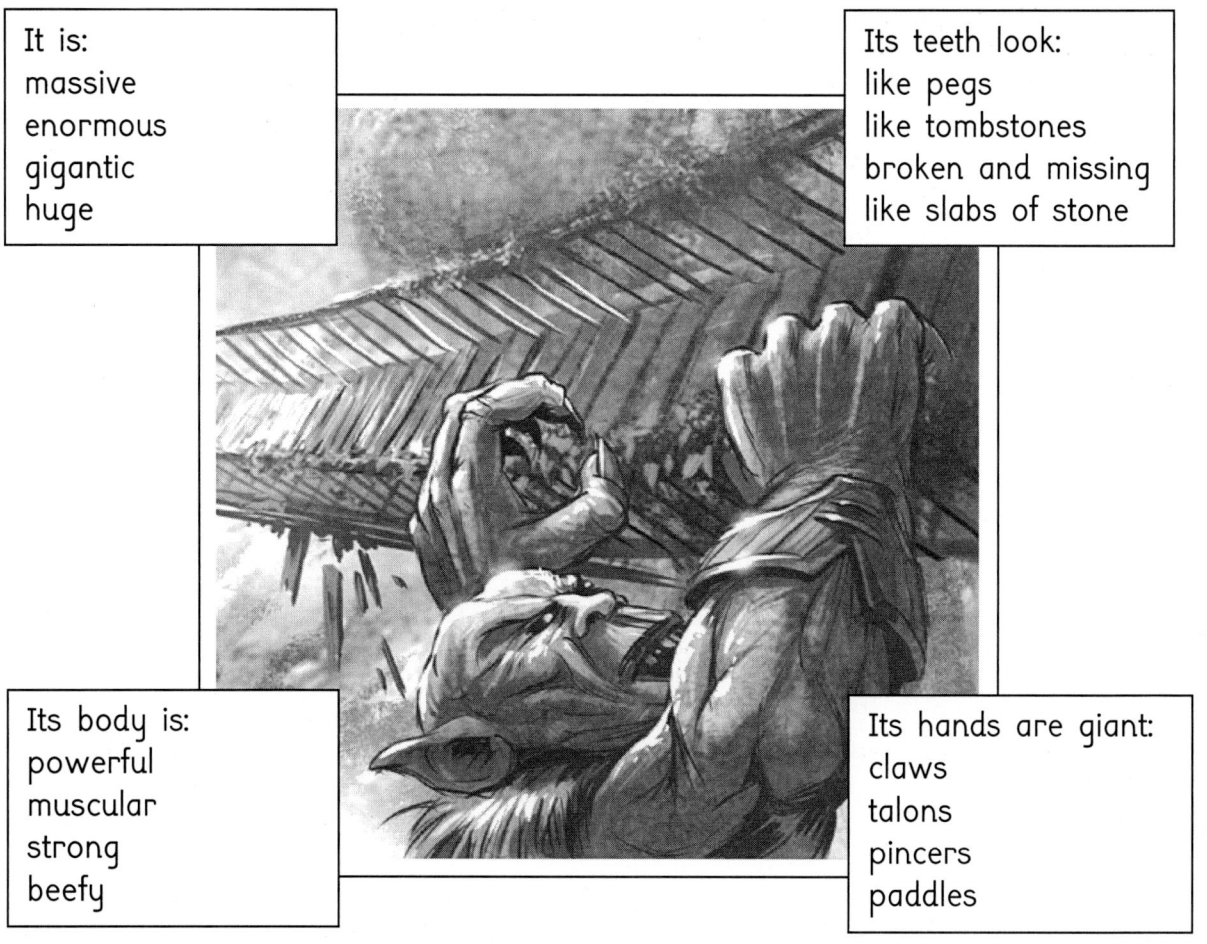

Its body is:
powerful
muscular
strong
beefy

Its hands are giant:
claws
talons
pincers
paddles

Describe the ogre:

_____
_____
_____
_____
_____
_____
_____

Describe the ogre. You can use some of the words in the boxes. This sheet may be photocopied by the purchaser. © Phonic Books Ltd. 2011.

Book 5: Comprehension

Bellerophon and Pegasus – true or false?

Bell er o phon

Peg a sus

bri dle

Chi mer a

ser pent's

cel eb ra ted

suc cess

am bi tious

in sect

One Greek myth tells the story of how the hero Bellerophon captured Pegasus, the winged horse, with a golden bridle. The golden bridle tamed Pegasus so that Bellerophon could ride on his back. Bellerophon and Pegasus were sent on a mission by the king, to kill Chimera, the fire-breathing monster.

The Chimera was a three-headed monster. It had a lion's head, a serpent's head and a goat's head. Bellerophon took a spear and attached a bit of lead to it. As the Chimera opened its mouth to hurl a fire ball at them, Bellerophon threw the spear into its mouth. The lead melted in its belly and killed it.

Bellerophon was celebrated and he married the king's daughter. But his success made him arrogant and he decided he wanted to go up to the top of Mount Olympus and take his place with the gods. He mounted Pegasus and they flew up to Mount Olympus. Zeus, the king of the gods, became angry and sent an insect to sting Pegasus. The horse bucked and Bellerophon fell to his death.

Is it true?	yes	no
Pegasus was a winged horse.	☐	☐
Bellerophon captured Pegasus with a silver bridle.	☐	☐
Chimera had the head of a sheep, a snake and a lion.	☐	☐
The melted lead killed the Chimera.	☐	☐
Bellerophon thought he deserved to live with the gods.	☐	☐
Bellerophon died because he was too ambitious.	☐	☐

Read the text. Some multisyllable words are split for the reader. Now read the sentences below and tick the boxes according to whether they are true or false. This sheet may be photocopied by the purchaser. © Phonic Books Ltd. 2011.

Book 5: Extension activity: Bellerophon and Pegasus

Circle the words you think could describe Bellerophon:

cowardly   adventurous   boastful   brave   foolish

modest   arrogant   cocky   wise   vain   conceited

Circle the words you think could describe Zeus:

powerful   gentle   all-knowing   outraged   peaceful

angry   happy   forgiving   vengeful   agreeable

Cut out the strips of text and assemble in the right order:

After killing the Chimera, Bellerophon was celebrated and he married the king's daughter. But his success made him arrogant and he decided he wanted to go to the top of Mount Olympus and take his place with the gods.

One Greek myth tells the story of how the hero Bellerophon captured Pegasus, the winged horse, with a golden bridle. The golden bridle tamed Pegasus so that Bellerophon could ride on his back.

The Chimera was a three-headed monster. It had a lion's head, a serpent's head and a snake's head. Bellerophon took a spear and attached a bit of lead to it.

He mounted Pegasus and they flew up to Mount Olympus. Zeus, the king of the gods, became angry and sent an insect to sting Pegasus. The horse bucked and Bellerophon fell to his death.

Bellerophon and Pegasus were sent on a mission by the king, to kill Chimera, the fire-breathing monster.

As the Chimera opened its mouth to hurl a fire ball at them, Bellerophon threw the spear into its mouth. The lead melted in its belly and killed it.

This extension activity follows on from the previous sheet 'True or False?'. The teacher may need to discuss some of the new vocabulary with the learner. This sheet may be photocopied by the purchaser. © Phonic Books Ltd. 2011.

Book 5: Splitting multisyllable words with 'j' spellings 1a

jo ker	jo ker	<u>joker</u>
gen tle		_____
judge ment		_____
dam age		_____
le gend		_____
a djust		_____
vill age		_____
cart ridge		_____
gym nas tics		_____
re gim ent		_____
tra ge dy		_____
ge ol o gy		_____
man age ment		_____
priv il ege		_____

Split the words into syllables. Sound out the syllables as you write them in the grey rectangles. Then write the whole word, saying the syllables as you do. This sheet may be photocopied by the purchaser. © Phonic Books Ltd. 2011.

Book 5: Splitting multisyllable words with 'j' spellings 1b

joker   jo   ker   <u>joker</u>

gentle

judgement

damage

legend

adjust

village

cartridge

gymnastics

regiment

tragedy

geology

management

privilege

Split the words into syllables. Sound out the syllables as you write them in the grey rectangles. Then write the whole word, saying the syllables as you do. This sheet may be photocopied by the purchaser. © Phonic Books Ltd. 2011.

Book 5: Stepping stones game: 'j'

START — **FINISH**

- joke
- gel
- judge
- edge
- wage
- cottage
- gem
- hedge
- grudge
- giant
- adjust
- dodge
- gentle
- jackal
- tragic
- village
- legible
- general
- manage
- badge
- adjective
- major
- ginger
- stage
- logic
- magic
- lodge
- bridge

Book 5: 4-in-a-row game: 'j'

jolly	dodge	gel	whinge	adjust
giraffe	savage	nudge	legend	judge
major	ridge	gentle	wedge	manage
village	tragic	mange	badge	energy
grudge	giant	dredge	magic	general
gorge	lodge	sledge	logic	gerbil
ginger	stage	range	germ	bridge

Play with two sets of coloured counters. Two players take turns to read the word and put a counter on the word. The winner is the first to get four of his or her counters in a row. The winner places a counter on a talisman. The game is played four times until all the talismans are covered. This sheet may be photocopied by the purchaser.
© Phonic Books Ltd. 2011.

Book 6: The Sphinx

Questions for discussion

Chapter 1

1. Zak and Mim walk in a canyon made of coloured sandstone. When a shaft of light lit up the canyon, "The effect was a symphony of pinks and yellows". Explain this in your own words. (pg 1)
2. Zak tried to decipher the symbols carved in the stone. What does 'decipher' mean? (pg 2)

Chapter 2

1. Why did they think the Sphinx may be a phantom? (pg 3)
2. What did they need to do in order to pass the Sphinx? (pg 4)

Chapter 3

1. Why do you think there were bones on the ground? (pg 5)
2. What was the riddle and what was the answer to it? (pgs 6 and 7)

Chapter 4

1. Why do you think the Sphinx did not let them pass? (pg 8)
2. Why did the Sphinx want the talisman? (pg 8)

Chapter 5

1. Why was Samson cross in the end? (pg 10)

These questions can be discussed after reading the text. They are intended to develop speaking and listening skills and comprehension. This sheet may be photocopied by the purchaser. © Phonic Books Ltd. 2011.

Book 6: Blending and segmenting: 'f'

flip	f	l	i	p		
stuff						
photo						
laugh						
effect						
dolphin						
cough						
muffin						
graphic						
tough						
suffer						
sphinx						
enough						

Blend the sounds into a word. Segment the word into sounds by writing one sound in each square. This sheet may be photocopied by the purchaser. © Phonic Books Ltd. 2011.

Book 6: Reading and sorting words with 'f' spellings

f	ff	ph	gh

frost	cuff	phone	laugh
photo	phase	gruff	food
phantom	sniff	rough	elephant
cough	dolphin	staff	sphinx
bluffing	frantic	flint	graph
enough	draught	puffin	orphan
physical	fluff	tough	sphere
fragment	trophy	coffin	triumph

Photocopy this page onto card and cut out the words. Read and sort the cards out according to the 'f' headings at the top of the page. This sheet may be photocopied by the purchaser. © Phonic Books Ltd. 2011.

Book 6: Spelling: 'f'

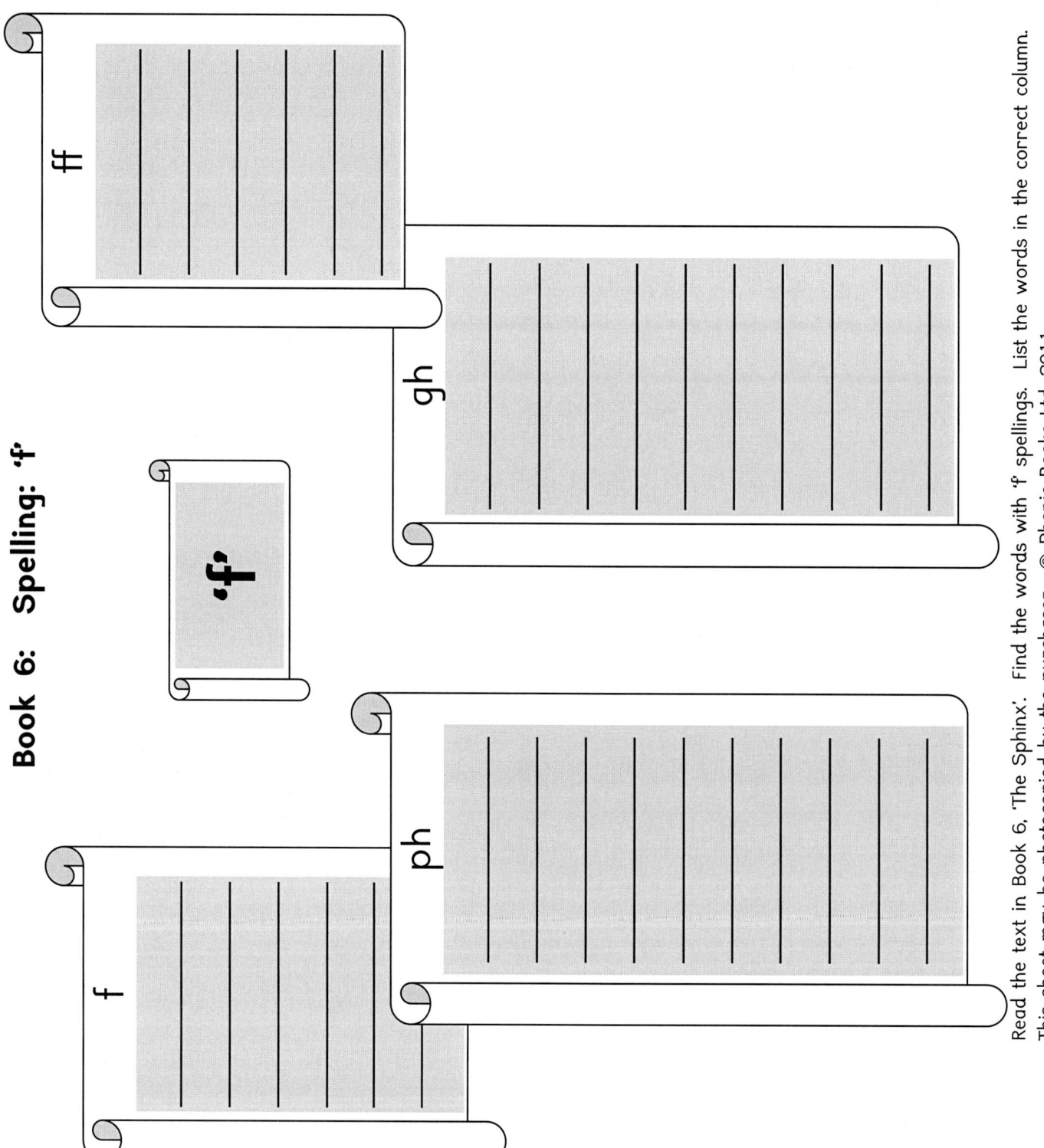

Read the text in Book 6, 'The Sphinx'. Find the words with 'f' spellings. List the words in the correct column. This sheet may be photocopied by the purchaser. © Phonic Books Ltd. 2011.

Book 6: Reading and spelling

The riddle was tough. But Mim cracked it. The Sphinx yelled "Enough! Give me that talisman. It will be my trophy!" Zak and Mim turned to run. The rough walls began to move. They could hear the Sphinx laughing.

The _ _ _ _ was _ _ _. But _ _ _ _ _ _ _ _ _. The _ _ _ _ _ "_ _ _ _ _ _ _ _ _! Give me _ _ _ _ _ _ _ _ _ _. It _ _ _ _ be my _ _ _ _ _!" Zak _ _ _ _ _ _ _ _ _ _ _ to _ _ _. The _ _ _ _ walls _ _ _ _ _ to _ _ _. They _ _ _ _ _ _ _ _ the _ _ _ _ _ _ _ _ _ _.

Copy the text in the top scroll to the bottom scroll. Write a sound on each line e.g.: t r o ph y. This activity can also be used for dictation. This sheet may be photocopied by the purchaser. © Phonic Books Ltd. 2011.

Book 6: Is it true?

How many untruths can you spot in the text?

When Zak and Mim walked into the canyon, they saw a symphony of blue and green coloured sandstone. Then they saw a hut. The atmosphere was magical. Zak tried to decipher some carvings on the wall. Suddenly, they saw a Sphinx. They didn't know if it was a phantom or if it was real. The Sphinx had a rough voice. It would not let them pass unless they could answer a tough riddle. When Mim solved the riddle, it demanded that Zak hand over the talisman as a trophy. When Zak said "NO!", the canyon walls began to crush them. Zak shape shifted into an elephant and they ran out as fast as they could.

How many untruths did you find? ☐

Read this text after reading Book 6, 'The Sphinx'. Underline the parts which are not true to the story in the book. Count the untruths and write the number in the box. This sheet may be photocopied by the purchaser. © Phonic Books Ltd 2011.

Book 6: Writing

The Sphinx – what is it like?

It looks:
angry
bad tempered
hostile
aggresive

Its eyes are like:
emeralds
green flames
green poison
toxic slime

Its wings are like:
feathery branches
palm trees
a storm brewing
a vulture's

It speaks:
coldly
in a cocky way
aggressively
arrogantly

Describe the Sphinx:
_____
_____
_____
_____
_____
_____

Describe the Sphinx. You can use some of the words in the boxes. This sheet may be photocopied by the purchaser. © Phonic Books Ltd. 2011.

Book 6: Comprehension

The sphinx – true or false?

trad i tion

ser pent

mer ci less

inn o cent

Oe di pus

crea ture

ad ult

Pha raoh

cul tures

In the Greek tradition, a sphinx was a monster with the body of a lion, the head of a beautiful woman and the tail of a serpent. The sphinx was a cruel and merciless monster. She would devour innocent travellers if they could not answer her riddles.

There is a famous Greek myth about Oedipus and the Sphinx. Oedipus was travelling when the Sphinx blocked his path. In order to pass, he had to answer this riddle:

"Which creature in the morning goes on four legs, at midday on two, and in the evening upon three, and the more legs it has, the weaker it be?" Oedipus solved the riddle. He answered: "Man – who crawls on all fours as a baby, then walks on two feet as an adult, and then walks with a cane in old age." The Sphinx was so angry that it leapt off its high rock and died.

In ancient Egypt, a sphinx had the head of a man or sometimes a Pharaoh. It was a good creature who guarded temples and tombs. The sphinx can be found in Asian cultures too.

Is it true?   yes   no

A sphinx always has the head of a woman.   ☐   ☐

In the Greek tradition, the sphinx was evil.   ☐   ☐

Only Oedipus knew the answer to the riddle.   ☐   ☐

The riddle is about different times in a man's life. ☐   ☐

In ancient Egypt, the sphinx was a bad creature. ☐   ☐

The sphinx appears in many cultures.   ☐   ☐

Read the text. Some multisyllable words are split for the reader. Now read the sentences below and tick the boxes according to whether they are true or false. This sheet may be photocopied by the purchaser. © Phonic Books Ltd. 2011.

Book 6: Extension activity: Riddles

Cut out the riddles and match them to the answers below.

There are two sisters: one gives birth to the other and she, in turn, gives birth to the first. What are they?	I am as big as an elephant but I am lighter than a feather. What am I?
No sooner spoken than broken. What is it?	A man went out for a walk when it started to rain. He did not have an umbrella or a hat. His clothes were soaked yet not a single hair on his head got wet. How could this happen?
What God never sees, what a king rarely sees but what we see all the time. What is it?	They have not flesh, nor feathers, nor bones nor scales and yet they have fingers and thumbs of their own. What are they?
It is as light as a feather yet no man can hold it for long. What is it?	It runs forever but never moves at all. It has not lungs or throat but still a mighty roaring call. What is it?

a waterfall	breath
the man was bald	day and night
gloves	an equal
the wind	silence

This extension activity follows on from the previous sheet 'True or False?'. This sheet may be photocopied by the purchaser. © Phonic Books Ltd. 2011.

Book 6: Splitting multisyllable words with 'f' spellings 1a

frost ed	frost	ed		frosted
fluff y				_____
laugh ing				_____
pho ney				_____
toff ee				_____
rough ly				_____
phan tom				_____
e nough				_____
par a graph				_____
sym pho ny				_____
ge o graph y				_____
em phas is				_____
mi cro phone				_____
or phan age				_____

Split the words into syllables. Sound out the syllables as you write them in the grey rectangles. Then write the whole word, saying the syllables as you do. This sheet may be photocopied by the purchaser. © Phonic Books Ltd. 2011.

Book 6: Splitting multisyllable words with 'f' spellings 1b

Word	Syllable 1	Syllable 2	Syllable 3	Syllable 4	Whole word
frosted	frost	ed			frosted
fluffy					_____
laughing					_____
phoney					_____
toffee					_____
roughly					_____
phantom					_____
enough					_____
paragraph					_____
symphony					_____
geography					_____
emphasis					_____
microphone					_____
orphanage					_____

Split the words into syllables. Sound out the syllables as you write them in the grey rectangles. Then write the whole word, saying the syllables as you do. This sheet may be photocopied by the purchaser. © Phonic Books Ltd. 2011.

Book 6: Stepping stones game: 'f'

START → **FINISH**

- flags
- coffin
- laugh
- photo
- coffee
- cough
- phone
- nephew
- tough
- phantom
- frantic
- puffing
- effort
- rough
- physics
- phase
- puffin
- enough
- triumph
- sphinx
- elephant
- trough
- draught
- graph
- graphics
- physical
- dolphin
- trophy

Book 6: 4-in-a-row game: 'f'

fig	bluff	phase	tough	photo
dolphin	Philip	stuff	trophy	rough
sphinx	flips	enough	graph	offend
coffin	sphere	defend	triumph	orphan
phantom	physics	phoney	affect	trough
griffin	foolish	draught	shuffle	muffin
phone	cough	office	frankly	laugh

Play with two sets of coloured counters. Two players take turns to read the word and put a counter on the word. The winner is the first to get four of his or her counters in a row. The winner places a counter on a talisman. The game is played four times until all the talismans are covered. This sheet may be photocopied by the purchaser.
© Phonic Books Ltd. 2011.

Book 7: Sticky Adventure

Questions for discussion

Chapter 1

1. Why did Mim feel a mixture of anger and resentment when Zak went off exploring? (pg 2)

Chapter 2

1. What did Zak see when he entered the cave? (pg 4)
2. What are stalagmites and stalactites? (pg 4)
3. Why are they described as sandcastles? (pg 4)

Chapter 3

1. What was the rasping sound that Zak could hear? (pg 6)
2. What were the wet pools in the caves? (pg 6)

Chapter 4

1. Why couldn't Zak escape from the cave? (pg 7)

Chapter 5

1. How did Mim avoid the slime pools? (pg 9)
2. How did the ant defeat the giant slug? (pg 11)

These questions can be discussed after reading the text. They are intended to develop speaking and listening skills and comprehension. This sheet may be photocopied by the purchaser. © Phonic Books Ltd. 2011.

Book 7: Blending and segmenting: suffix 'cher'

capture	c	a	p	ture
mixture				
lecture				
future			ture	
nature			ture	
creature				
adventure						
picture				
gesture				
structure						
culture				
miniature						
vulture				

Blend the sounds into a word. Segment the word into sounds by writing one sound in each square.
This sheet may be photocopied by the purchaser. © Phonic Books Ltd. 2011.

Book 7: Reading words with the suffix <ture> 1a

capture	rapture	fixture	adventure
future	mixture	nature	picture
feature	culture	posture	gesture
literature	creature	departure	lecture
puncture	structure	furniture	caricature
venture	vulture	agriculture	moisture
torture	fracture	nurture	pasture

Book 7: Reading words with the suffix <ture> 1b

capture	rapture	fixture	adventure
future	mixture	nature	picture
feature	culture	posture	gesture
literature	creature	departure	lecture
puncture	structure	furniture	caricature
venture	vulture	agriculture	moisture
torture	fracture	nurture	pasture

Photocopy this page onto card and cut out the words. Practise reading words with the suffix <ture>. This sheet may be photocopied by the purchaser. © Phonic Books Ltd. 2011.

Book 7: Spelling with the 'cher' suffix

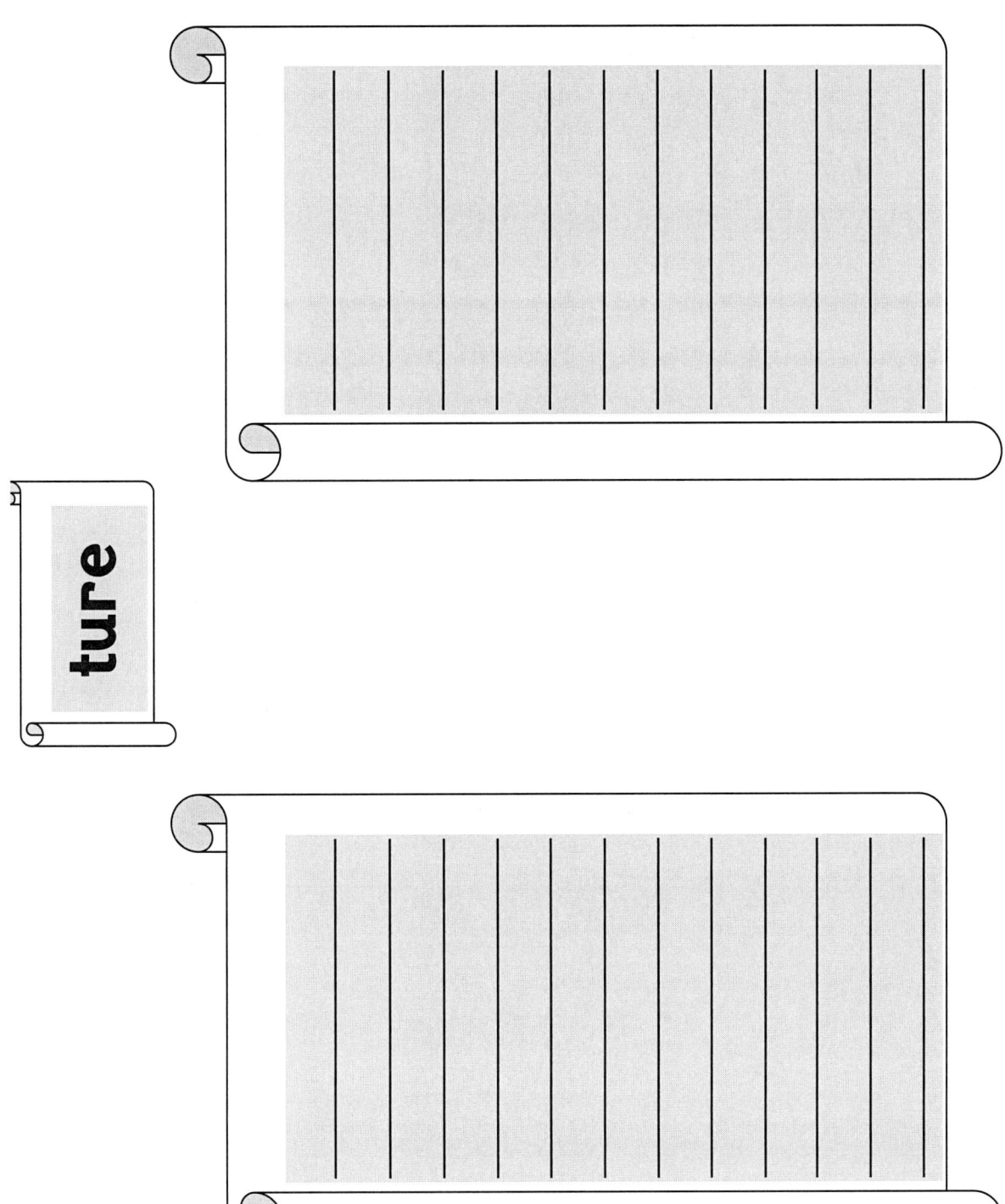

Read the text in Book 7, 'Sticky Adventure'. Find the words with the <ture> suffix. List the words in the column. © Phonic Books Ltd. 2011.
This sheet may be photocopied by the purchaser.

Book 7: Reading and spelling

Zak loved nature and adventure. He also liked danger. Mim tried to lecture him about it but it was no use. He was captured by a giant slug. He thought he was going to die and his future flashed before him.

Zak loved _ _ ___   _ _ _
_ _ _ _ _ _ ___. He _ _ _
_ _ _ _   _ _ _ ___. _ _ _
_ _ _ _   to   _ _ _ ___
_ _ _   _ _ _ _   it   _ _ _
_ _   _ _ _   no   ‿_ _ _.
He   _ _ _   _ _ _ ___ _   by
a   _ _ _ _ _   _ _ _ _. He
__ ___ _   he was   _ _ _ _
to   _ _   and his   _ _ ___
_ _ _ ___   before   _ _ _.

Copy the text in the top scroll to the bottom scroll. Write a sound on each line e.g.: h i m. Where there is a target suffix, write the whole suffix on the line e.g.: f u ture. This activity can also be used for dictation. This sheet may be photocopied by the purchaser.
© Phonic Books Ltd. 2011.

Book 7: Is it true?

How many untruths can you spot in the text?

Zak looked at the valley around him. He loved nature. He set off looking for another adventure. He came to a cave hidden behind a wall. He ventured into the dark cave. Zak saw amazing structures, like giant sandcastles.

He stepped into a sticky pool of pink slime. Then he was captured by a giant frog creature. In the meantime, Mim got worried. She entered the cave. She saw Zak stuck in a funny posture. She was careful not to get captured by stepping over the slime pools. Mim took the talisman from Zak and turned him into an acid-squirting ant. The slug creature dissolved. It was not a pretty picture.

How many untruths did you find? ☐

Read this text after reading Book 7 'Sticky Adventure'. Underline the parts which are not true to the story in the book. Count the untruths and write the number in the box. This sheet may be photocopied by the purchaser. © Phonic Books Ltd. 2011.

Book 7: Writing

The giant slug – what is it like?

It looks:
disgusting
repulsive
revolting
hideous

Its body is:
spotty
speckled
squashy
blobby

Its tentacles:
grope
feel about
fumble
twitch

Its jaws are like:
a shark's jaw
a toothed monster
a giant tadpole
a gaping hole

Describe the giant slug:
_____
_____
_____
_____
_____
_____
_____

Describe the giant slug. You can use some of the words in the boxes. This sheet may be photocopied by the purchaser. © Phonic Books Ltd. 2011.

Book 7: Comprehension

Amazing ants – true or false?

a maz ing

suc cess ful

e vol ved

An tarc ti ca

so ci et y

diff er ent

ster ile

fer tile

comm u ni cate

en vi ron ments

de fend ing

Ants are amazing and very successful creatures. Ants evolved from wasp-like creatures 130 million years ago. There are thought to be 22,000 species of ant that live almost everywhere on earth except Antartica and some small remote islands.

Ants are social insects that live in colonies. These can consist of a few dozen ants or millions of individuals. Their society is highly organised with different ants having different jobs to do.

In the large colonies, there will be sterile, wingless females who are 'workers' or 'soldiers'. There will be some fertile males called 'drones' and one or more fertile females called 'queens'.

The reasons why ants are so successful are that they work together, can communicate with each other, and are even known to be able to solve problems. They adapt to new environments and find new food sources. They are also very good at fighting and defending their colonies.

Is it true?	yes	no
Ants exist in Antartica.	☐	☐
They evolved from creatures that looked like wasps.	☐	☐
Ants are solitary animals.	☐	☐
The drones are fertile male ants.	☐	☐
Different ants have different jobs in the colony.	☐	☐
Ants are unable to survive and will become extinct.	☐	☐

Read the text. Some multisyllable words are split for the reader. Now read the sentences below and tick the boxes according to whether they are true or false. This sheet may be photocopied by the purchaser. © Phonic Books Ltd. 2011.

Book 7: Extension activity: Fill in the missing words

Fill in the missing words so that the text makes sense.

Amazing ants

Ants _____ amazing and very successful creatures. Ants evolved _____ wasp-like creatures 130 million years ago. There are thought to be 22,000 species _____ ant that live almost everywhere on earth except Antartica and _____ small remote islands.

Ants are social _____ that live in colonies. These can consist of a few dozen ants or millions of _____. Their society ____ highly organised with different ants having _____ jobs to do.

In large colonies, there _____ be sterile, wingless females who are 'workers' or 'soldiers'. There will be some fertile males called 'drones' and one or more fertile _____ called 'queens'.

The reasons why ants are so successful are that they work _____, can communicate with each other, and are even known to be able to solve _____. They adapt to new environments and _____ new food sources. They are also very good at fighting and defending _____ colonies.

This extension activity follows on from the previous sheet 'True or False?'. Any words are acceptable on the blank line as long as the text makes sense. This sheet may be photocopied by the purchaser. © Phonic Books Ltd. 2011.

Book 7: Splitting multisyllable words with <ture> suffix 1a

na ture | na | ture | nature

cap ture | | | _____

cul ture | | | _____

fea ture | | | _____

punc ture | | | _____

pic ture | | | _____

de par ture | | | _____

ad ven ture | | | _____

fur ni ture | | | _____

sig na ture | | | _____

car ic a ture | | | _____

fix ture | | | _____

ag ri cul ture | | | _____

struc ture | | | _____

Split the words into syllables. Sound out the syllables as you write them in the grey rectangles. Then write the whole word, saying the syllables as you do. This sheet may be photocopied by the purchaser. © Phonic Books Ltd. 2011.

Book 7: Splitting multisyllable words with <ture> suffix 1b

nature	na	ture		nature
capture				_____
culture				_____
feature				_____
puncture				_____
picture				_____
departure				_____
adventure				_____
furniture				_____
signature				_____
caricature				_____
fixture				_____
agriculture				_____
structure				_____

Split the words into syllables. Sound out the syllables as you write them in the grey rectangles. Then write the whole word, saying the syllables as you do. This sheet may be photocopied by the purchaser. © Phonic Books Ltd. 2011.

Book 7: Stepping stones game: <ture>

START → adventure → capture → mixture → future → picture → posture → moisture → venture → fixture → denture → culture → nature → lecture → departure → feature → creature → gesture → vulture → rapture → torture → puncture → furniture → caricature → literature → structure → pasture → nurture → fracture → **FINISH**

Book 7: 4-in-a-row game: <ture>

rapture	nature	adventure	picture	mixture
fixture	creature	nature	torture	future
fracture	posture	lecture	venture	denture
feature	stature	capture	gesture	culture
nurture	picture	pasture	torture	moisture
departure	gesture	venture	puncture	structure

Play with two sets of coloured counters. Two players take turns to read the word and put a counter on the word. The winner is the first to get four of his or her counters in a row. The winner places a counter on a talisman. The game is played four times until all the talismans are covered. This sheet may be photocopied by the purchaser.
© Phonic Books Ltd. 2011.

Book 8: Dangerous Direction

Questions for discussion

Chapter 1

1. Which word on the map attracted Zak's attention and why? (pg 2)
2. Why did Zak roll up the map quickly? (pg 2)

Chapter 2

1. Mim had a passion for grapes. What does it mean when you have a passion for something? (pg 3)
2. Why didn't Zak tell Mim about his dream? (pg 4)

Chapter 3

1. Mim felt she had to defend her reputation. What does it mean to defend one's reputation? (pg 6)
2. How did Zak react when Mim fell into the rushing river? (pg 7)

Chapter 4

1. How did Samson rescue Mim? (pg 8)
2. Why did Zak look at the Kelpie with revulsion? (pg 9)

Chapter 5

1. What did Zak confess to Mim? (pg 12)
2. What do you think about Mim's response? (pg 12)

These questions can be discussed after reading the text. They are intended to develop speaking and listening skills and comprehension. This sheet may be photocopied by the purchaser. © Phonic Books Ltd. 2011.

Book 8: Blending and segmenting: suffix 'shun'

action	a	c	tion		
mission					
mansion					
Alsatian					
magician					
lotion					
passion					
tension					
Dalmatian					
physician					
ambition					
discussion					
pension					

Blend the sounds into a word. Segment the word into sounds by writing one sound in each square. This sheet may be photocopied by the purchaser. © Phonic Books Ltd. 2011.

Book 8: Reading and sorting words with the suffix 'shun' 1a

| tion | sion | ssion | tian | cian |

action	mansion	mission	Alsatian
politician	nation	compassion	session
passion	pension	ration	impression
station	reaction	tension	admission
obsession	motion	discussion	permission
aggression	mention	fraction	Egyptian
extension	addition	revulsion	electrician
technician	inspection	attention	profession

Photocopy this page onto card and cut out the words. Read and sort the cards out according to the 'shun' headings at the top of the page. This sheet may be photocopied by the purchaser. © Phonic Books Ltd. 2011.

Book 8: Reading and sorting words with the suffix 'shun' 1b

| tion | sion | ssion | tian | cian |

action	mansion	mission	Alsatian
politician	nation	compassion	session
passion	pension	ration	impression
station	reaction	tension	admission
obsession	motion	discussion	permission
aggression	mention	fraction	Egyptian
extension	addition	revulsion	electrician
technician	inspection	attention	profession

Photocopy this page onto card and cut out the words. Read and sort the cards out according to the 'shun' headings at the top of the page. This sheet may be photocopied by the purchaser. © Phonic Books Ltd. 2011.

Book 8: Spelling with the 'shun' suffix

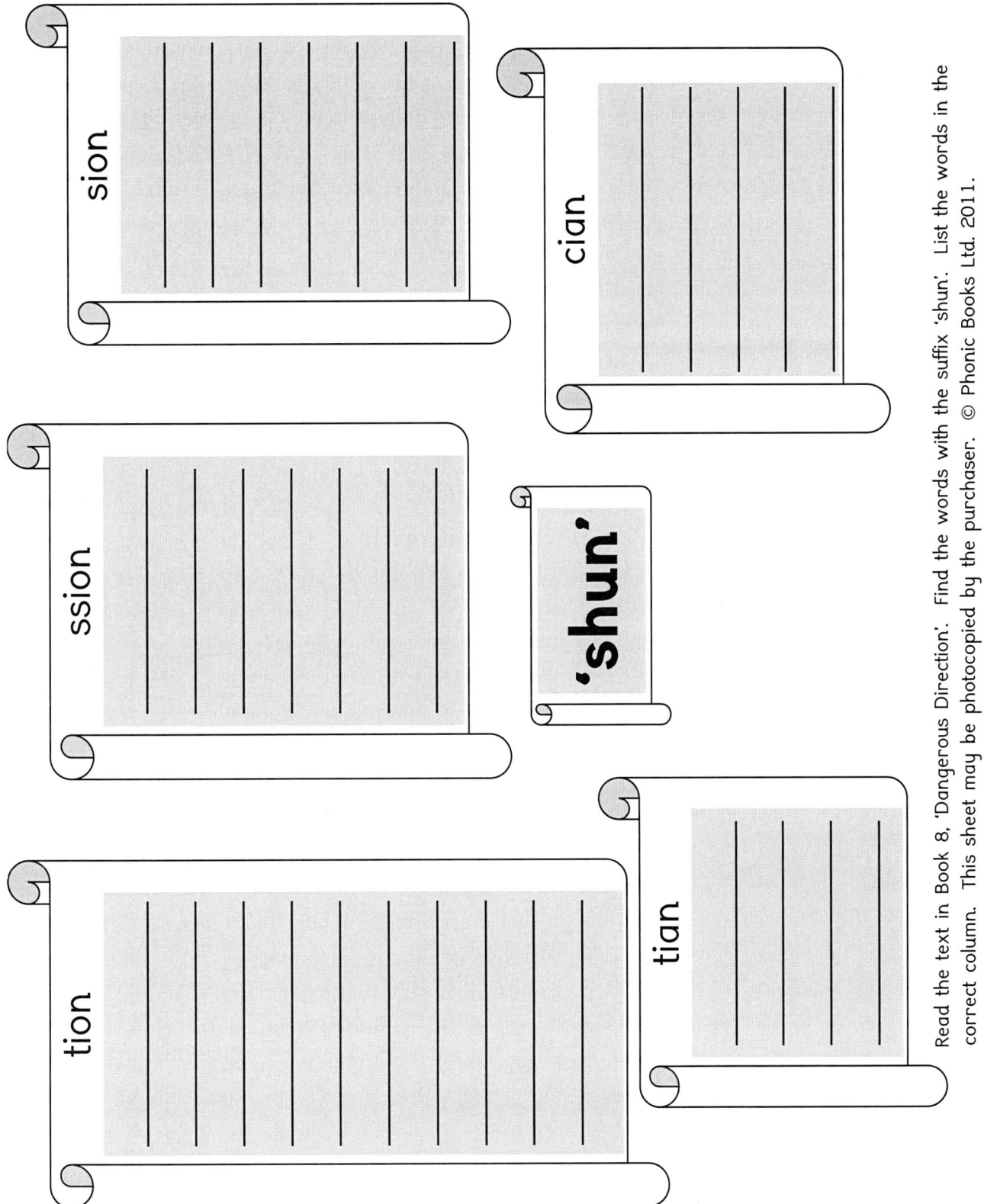

Read the text in Book 8, 'Dangerous Direction'. Find the words with the suffix 'shun'. List the words in the correct column. © Phonic Books Ltd. 2011.

Book 8: Reading and spelling

Zak had a dream. In his dream, the Dark Master looked like a magician. The Dark Master said the talisman was his possession and that he would destroy civilization. Zak did not mention his dream to Mim.

Zak _ _ _   _   _ _ _ _.
In _ _ _   _ _ _ _, the _ _ _   _ _ _ _
_ _ _ _ _ like a _ _ _ _ _ _.
The _ _ _ Master _ _ _ the
_ _ _ _ _ _ _ _ was his
_ _ _ _ _ _ _ _ and that he
_ _ _ _   _ _ _ _ _
_ _ _ _ _ _ _ _ _. Zak
_ _   _ _   _ _ _ _ _   _ _ _   _ _ _
his _ _ _ _   _ _   _ _ _.

Copy the text in the top scroll to the bottom scroll. Write a sound on each line e.g.: h i m.
Where there is a target suffix, write the whole suffix on the line e.g.: m e n tion.
This activity can also be used for dictation. This sheet may be photocopied by the purchaser.
© Phonic Books Ltd. 2011.

Book 8: Is it true?

How many untruths can you spot in the text?

Mim and Zak had a discussion about which direction they should take. Zak decided to take action without asking Mim. On the way, they stopped to eat passion fruits. Then they fell asleep. Zak dreamed of the Dark Master who looked like a martian. He was going to destroy civilization. Zak did not mention the dream to Mim. When they saw a tree that had fallen across the river, Zak challenged Mim to a duel, which she had to accept without hesitation. Mim lost her footing and fell into the rushing waters. Samson turned into a Dalmation dog and rescued her. Then a horrible Kelpie dragged him under. Zak became a river dolphin and defeated the Kelpie.

How many untruths did you find?

Read this text after reading Book 8 'Dangerous Direction'. Underline the parts which are not true to the book. Count the untruths and write the number in the box. This sheet may be photocopied by the purchaser. © Phonic Books Ltd. 2011.

Book 8: Writing

What happened to Samson?

Samson ran to rescue Mim. He:
ran
galloped
raced ... to Mim.

Samson plunged into the water like:
a hippo
a whale
a seal

The Kelpie:
pushed him under
pulled him under
held him under
dragged him under

Samson:
thrashed about
gasped for air
kicked about
brayed in panic

Describe what happened to Samson:

_____
_____
_____
_____
_____
_____
_____

Describe what happened to Samson. You can use some of the words in the boxes. This sheet may be photocopied by the purchaser. © Phonic Books Ltd. 2011.

Book 8: Comprehension

The baiji river dolphin – true or false?

dol phin

Yang tze

diff er ent

mar ine

sa cred

en dan gered

re sult

en tan gled

de clared

ex tinct

The baiji was a river dolphin that could only be found in the River Yangtze in China.

River dolphins are freshwater dolphins, which live in rivers. They look different to marine dolphins that live in the sea. They have longer snouts than marine dolphins and smaller eyes and poor eyesight as they swim in dark, muddy rivers.

Once the baiji were sacred animals but then people began hunting them. They became endangered as a result of river fishing. They would get entangled in fishing nets. With many boats on the river, the river became polluted.

In 2006, leading experts in the field could not find a single baiji dolphin. The baiji was declared extinct.

This was the first time that a water mammal had become extinct in 50 years.

Is it true? yes no

The baiji swam in rivers all over the world. ☐ ☐

River dolphins like salty water. ☐ ☐

River dolphins have bad eyesight. ☐ ☐

The baiji used to be protected. ☐ ☐

The river got dirty from all the boats on it. ☐ ☐

The baiji is now extinct and cannot be found anywhere. ☐ ☐

Read the text. Some multisyllable words are split for the reader. Now read the sentences below and tick the boxes according to whether they are true or false. This sheet may be photocopied by the purchaser. © Phonic Books Ltd. 2011.

Book 8: Extension activity: Save the River Dolphins!

Other species of river dolphins are also endangered. Find out more about them and make a poster showing how people should protect them. You can use the image of the extinct baiji.

This extension activity follows on from the previous sheet 'True or False?'. This sheet may be photocopied by the purchaser. © Phonic Books Ltd. 2011.

Book 8: Splitting multisyllable words with 'shun' suffix 1a

ac tion	ac | tion	action
na tion	☐ ☐	_____
man sion	☐ ☐	_____
mi ssion	☐ ☐	_____
Al sa tian	☐ ☐ ☐	_____
frac tion	☐ ☐	_____
pa ssion	☐ ☐	_____
ma gi cian	☐ ☐ ☐	_____
pro fe ssion	☐ ☐ ☐	_____
conn ec tion	☐ ☐ ☐	_____
Dal ma tian	☐ ☐ ☐	_____
in for ma tion	☐ ☐ ☐ ☐	_____
el ec tri cian	☐ ☐ ☐ ☐	_____
poss e ssion	☐ ☐ ☐	_____

Split the words into syllables. Sound out the syllables as you write them in the grey rectangles. Then write the whole word, saying the syllables as you do. This sheet may be photocopied by the purchaser. © Phonic Books Ltd. 2011.

Book 8: Splitting multisyllable words with 'shun' suffix 1b

Word	Syllables	Whole word
action	ac / tion	action
nation		
mansion		
mission		
Alsatian		
fraction		
passion		
magician		
profession		
connection		
Dalmatian		
information		
electrician		
possession		

Split the words into syllables. Sound out the syllables as you write them in the grey rectangles. Then write the whole word, saying the syllables as you do. This sheet may be photocopied by the purchaser. © Phonic Books Ltd. 2011.

Book 8: Stepping stones game: 'shun'

START → action → mission → relation → Alsatian → caption → tension → mention → politician → creation → nation → lotion → passion → mansion → motion → session → pension → Dalmatian → optician → attention → devotion → fiction → detention → magician → function → permission → tradition → obsession → admission → **FINISH**

This game is for 1–4 players. Play with counters and die. This sheet may be photocopied by the purchaser. © Phonic Books Ltd. 2011.

Book 8: 4-in-a-row game: 'shun'

caption	mission	relation	Alsatian	action
tension	mention	politician	creation	nation
lotion	passion	mansion	motion	session
pension	fraction	optician	attention	devotion
function	magician	detention	addition	notion
fiction	admission	extension	obsession	tradition

Play with two sets of coloured counters. Two players take turns to read the word and put a counter on the word. The winner is the first to get four of his or her counters in a row. The winner places a counter on a talisman. The game is played four times until all the talismans are covered. This sheet may be photocopied by the purchaser.
© Phonic Books Ltd. 2011.

Book 9: Zak Tries Martial Arts

Questions for discussion

Chapter 1

1. What do think the artificial purple light coming from Volcano Island was? (pg 1)
2. What did Zak love to eat? (pg 2)
3. Why did Zak and Mim plan to cross the channel at night? (pg 2)

Chapter 2

1. Why did Mim say that the Dark Master would die from laughter? (pg 3)
2. How did Mim convince Samson to get on the raft? (pg 4)

Chapter 3

1. Why was there a mine on the island? (pg 6)
2. What does the word 'ore' mean? (pg 6)

Chapter 4

1. What did the guard look like? (pg 9)
2. How did he manage to control Zak, Mim and Samson? (pg 9)

Chapter 5

1. How did Zak turn himself into an anaconda? (pg 11)

These questions can be discussed after reading the text. They are intended to develop speaking and listening skills and comprehension. This sheet may be photocopied by the purchaser. © Phonic Books Ltd. 2011.

Book 9: Blending and segmenting: suffix 'shul'

social	s	o	cial			
martial						
special						
financial						
official						
essential						
potential						
artificial						
crucial						
torrential						
glacial						
racial						
facial						

Blend the sounds into a word. Segment the word into sounds by writing one sound in each square.
This sheet may be photocopied by the purchaser. © Phonic Books Ltd. 2011.

Book 9: Reading words with the suffix 'shul' 1a

cial	tial

official 1	glacial 2	essential 3	partial 4
racial 5	initial 6	influential 7	social 8
torrential 9	commercial 10	facial 11	confidential 12
crucial 13	provincial 14	especially 15	spatial 16
having influence on something or somebody 7	coming from an authority e.g. 'an official letter' 1	like a fast stream of water e.g. 'torrential rain' 9	relating to only a part of something 4
the beginning of something 6	very important and decisive 13	relating to dividing humans according to their race 5	relating to living in a community 8
to do with the face e.g. beauty treatment to face 11	absolutely necessary 3	has masses of ice 2	existing or happening in space 16
from a small place, unsophisticated 14	to do with buying and selling for profit 10	spoken or given in private 12	specifically e.g. 'I especially love vanilla ice cream' 15

Photocopy this page onto card and cut out the words and the definitions. Match the definitions to the words, using the numbers and stick them back to back. Read the cards with the 'shul' suffix and sort them into the two different spellings. This sheet may be photocopied by the purchaser. © Phonic Books Ltd. 2011.

Book 9: Reading words with the suffix 'shul' 1b

cial	tial

official	glacial	essential	partial
racial	initial	influential	social
torrential	commercial	facial	confidential
crucial	provincial	especially	spatial
relating to only a part of something	very important and decisive	having influence on something or somebody	relating to dividing humans according to their race
like a fast stream of water e.g. 'torrential rain'	to do with buying and selling for profit	to do with the face e.g. beauty treatment to face	coming from an authority e.g. 'an official letter'
existing or happening in space	the beginning of something	spoken or given in private	absolutely necessary
has masses of ice	from a small place, unsophisticated	specifically e.g. 'I especially love vanilla ice cream'	relating to living in a community

Photocopy this page onto card and cut out the words and the definitions. Match the definitions to the words and stick them back to back. Read the words with the 'shul' suffix and sort into the two different spellings. This sheet may be photocopied by the purchaser. © Phonic Books Ltd. 2011.

Book 9: Spelling with the 'shul' suffix

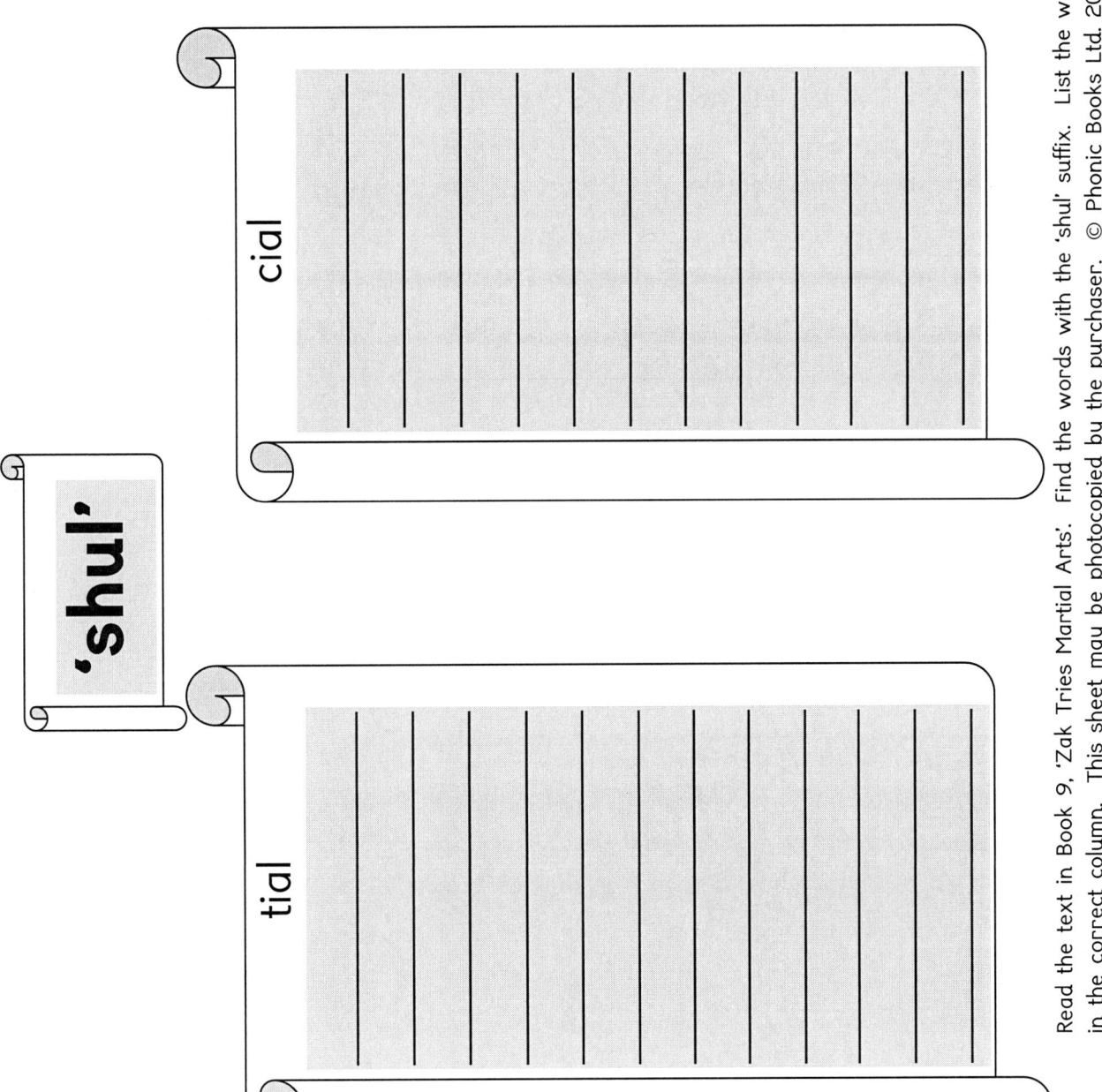

Read the text in Book 9, 'Zak Tries Martial Arts'. Find the words with the 'shul' suffix. List the words in the correct column. © Phonic Books Ltd. 2011.

Book 9: Blending and segmenting: suffix 'shus'

precious	p	r	e	cious	
delicious					
cautious					
suspicious					
fictitious					
vicious					
malicious					
gracious					
spacious					
vivacious					
noxious					
obnoxious					
conscious					

Blend the sounds into a word. Segment the word into sounds by writing one sound in each square.
This sheet may be photocopied by the purchaser.   © Phonic Books Ltd. 2011.

Book 9: Reading and sorting words with the suffix 'shus' 1a

tious	cious	ious	scious

cautious 1	conscious 2	delicious 3	pretentious 4
spacious 5	malicious 6	noxious 7	gracious 8
auspicious 9	tenacious 10	obnoxious 11	anxious 12
suspicious 13	precious 14	ferocious 15	vicious 16
to be kind 8	has lots of space 5	savage, fierce 15	careful 1
evil 6	favourable, with good fortune 9	aware 2	poisonous 7
to suspect something 13	valuable 14	worried or nervous 12	trying to make oneself look important 4
wicked and cruel 16	stubborn, holding on 10	very tasty 3	very unpleasant 11

Photocopy this page onto card and cut out the words and the definitions. Match the definitions to the words, using the numbers and stick them back to back. Read and sort the cards out according to the different spellings at the top of the page. This sheet may be photocopied by the purchaser. © Phonic Books Ltd. 2011.

Book 9: Reading and sorting words with the suffix 'shus' 1b

tious	cious	ious	scious

cautious	conscious	delicious	pretentious
spacious	malicious	noxious	gracious
auspicious	tenacious	obnoxious	anxious
suspicious	precious	ferocious	vicious
to be kind	has lots of space	savage, fierce	careful
evil	favourable, with good fortune	aware	poisonous
to suspect something	valuable	worried or nervous	trying make oneself look important
wicked and cruel	stubborn, holding on	very tasty	very unpleasant

Photocopy this page onto card and cut out the words and the definitions. Match the definitions to the words and stick them back to back. Read and sort the cards out according to the different spellings at the top of the page. This sheet may be photocopied by the purchaser. © Phonic Books Ltd. 2011.

Book 9: Spelling with the 'shus' suffix

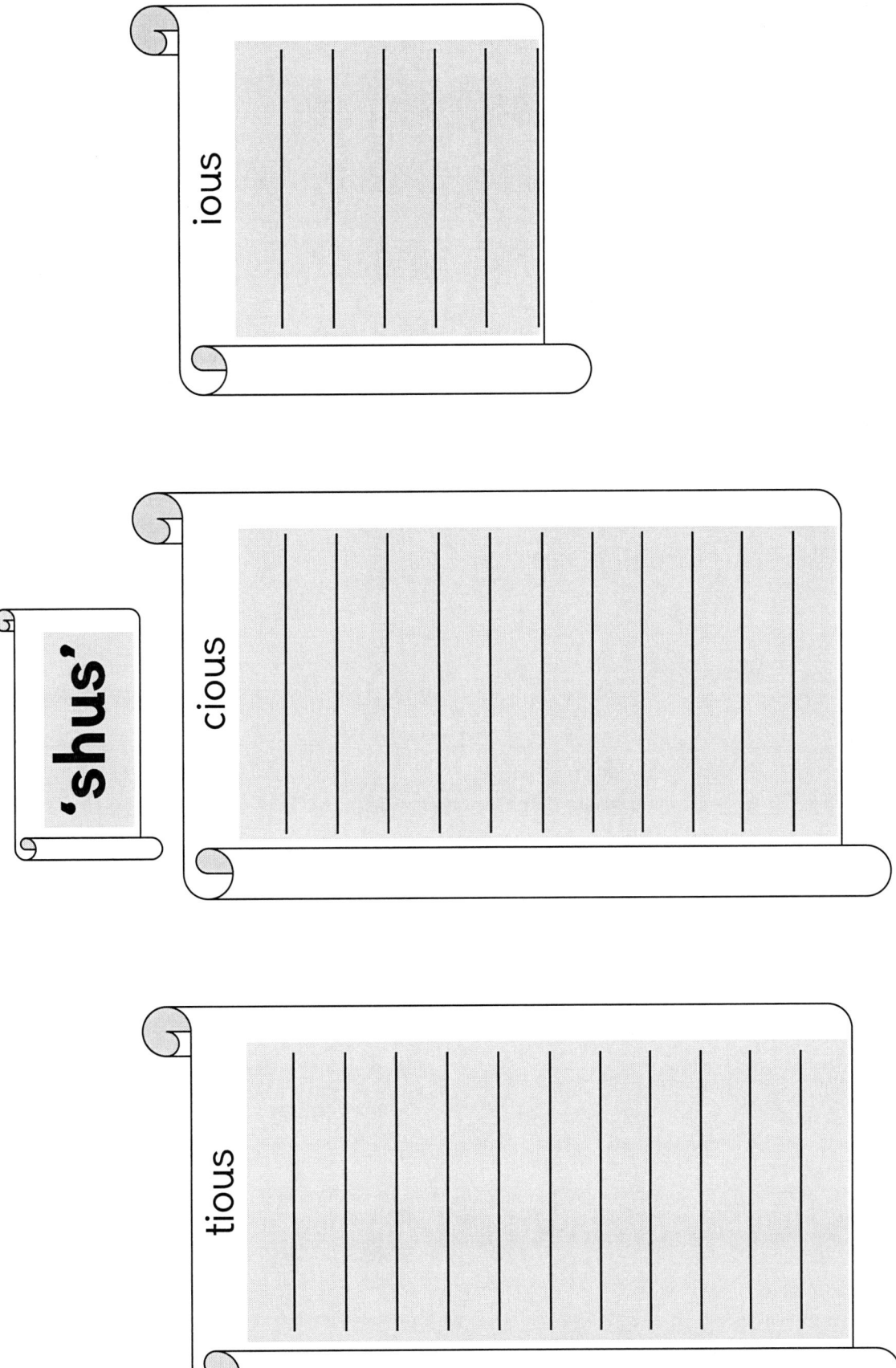

Read the text in Book 9, 'Zak Tries Martial Arts'. Find the words with the 'shus' suffix. List the words in the correct column. This sheet may be photocopied by the purchaser. © Phonic Books Ltd. 2011.

Book 9: Reading and spelling

Zak and Mim could see an artificial light glowing across the channel. It was essential to approach it cautiously. But a guard spotted them and hit Zak with his arm. He was vicious! Zak lay on the ground, unconscious.

Zak and Mim _ __ _ _ _ _

an _ _ _ _ _ _ __ _ _ _ _

_ _ __ _ __ across the

_ _ __ _ _ . It was

_ _ _ _ ___ to approach it

_ __ _ _ _ _. But a _ _ _ _

_ _ _ _ __ _ _ them and _ _ _

_ _ _ with _ _ _ __ _.

He was _ _ ___! Zak _ _ _

on the _ _ __ _ _,

_ _ _ _ _ ___.

Copy the text in the top scroll to the bottom scroll. Write a sound on each line e.g.: <u>h</u> <u>i</u> <u>m</u>.
Where there is a target suffix, write the whole suffix on the line e.g.: <u>s</u> <u>p</u> <u>e</u> <u>cial</u>.
This activity can also be used for dictation. This sheet may be photocopied by the purchaser.
© Phonic Books Ltd. 2011.

Book 9: Is it true?

How many untruths can you spot in the text?

Zak and Mim saw an artificial light glowing across the channel. Zak prepared for battle by practising his special martial arts moves. Mim laughed at him. Zak found a boat and Mim and Samson got in it cautiously. Mim was anxious. They stepped onto the island and walked cautiously up a steep path. They reached a mine where the Dark Master had dug for precious metals for his new talisman. Then they saw a ferocious three-armed guard. He knocked Zak unconscious. His vicious grip held Mim around the waist. Zak turned into an anaconda. It bit the guard and he collapsed and fell to the ground.

How many untruths did you find? [ ]

Read this text after reading Book 9 'Zak Tries Martial Arts'. Underline the parts which are not true to the book. Count the untruths and write the number in the box. This sheet may be photocopied by the purchaser. © Phonic Books Ltd. 2011.

Book 9: Writing

The guard – what was he like?

He looked like:
an ox
a bull
a minotaur
a mutant

His mouth was like:
a fish mouth
a gaping hole
a toothless tube
a black hole

His arms were like:
an octopus
a jellyfish
tentacles
worms

His eyes were like:
molten lava
fiery coals
laser beams
pools of hatred

Describe the guard:

_____
_____
_____
_____
_____
_____
_____

Describe the guard. You can use some of the words in the boxes. This sheet may be photocopied by the purchaser. © Phonic Books Ltd. 2011.

Book 9: Comprehension

The anaconda – true or false?

an ac on da

ven om ous

trop ic al

a quat ic

in clud ing

dom es tic

an im als

con strict or

con strict ing

swa llowed

in tim id a ting

dan ger ous

Anaconda

The anaconda is a large, non-venomous snake found in tropical South America.

The most famous anaconda is the green anaconda which is one of the world's largest snakes.

Anacondas are aquatic snakes. They live and hunt in water. They prey mostly on other animals that live in the water including water birds. They have been known to prey on domestic animals such as goats and ponies that come too close to the water's edge to drink.

Anacondas belong to the boa or 'constrictor' family. They hunt by 'constricting' their prey. They grasp their prey to hold it down. Then they quickly wrap their coils around it. They squeeze their prey so that it cannot breathe. The prey is swallowed whole and may take several days or weeks to digest.

Despite their intimidating size and muscle power, they are not dangerous to humans.

Is it true?	yes	no
The anaconda has a dangerous bite.	☐	☐
It lives in the water.	☐	☐
It can kill land animals that come to the water's edge.	☐	☐
It kills by strangling its prey.	☐	☐
The anaconda hunts every day.	☐	☐
Humans can be swallowed whole.	☐	☐

Read the text. Some multisyllable words are split for the reader. Now read the sentences below and tick the boxes according to whether they are true or false. This sheet may be photocopied by the purchaser. © Phonic Books Ltd. 2011.

Book 9: Extension activity: Fill in the missing words

Fill in the missing words so that the text makes sense.

The anaconda

The anaconda is a large, non-venomous _____ found in tropical South _____.

The most famous anaconda is the green anaconda which is one of the world's _____ snakes.

Anacondas are aquatic snakes. They live and hunt in _____. They prey mostly on other animals that live in the _____ including water _____. They have been known to prey on domestic animals such as _____ and ponies that come too close to the water's edge to _____.

Anacondas belong to the boa or 'constrictor' _____. They hunt by 'constricting' their prey. They grasp their _____ to hold it down. Then they quickly wrap their coils _____ it. They squeeze their prey so that it cannot _____. The prey is swallowed whole and may take several _____ or weeks to digest.

Despite their intimidating _____ and muscle power, they are not dangerous to _____.

This extension activity follows on from the previous sheet 'True or False?'. Any words are acceptable on the blank lines as long as the text makes sense. This sheet may be photocopied by the purchaser. © Phonic Books Ltd. 2011.

Book 9: Splitting multisyllable words with 'shul' suffix 1a

so cial	so	cial	<u>social</u>
fa cial			_____
ra cial			_____
par tial			_____
spe cial			_____
ess en tial			_____
off i cial			_____
in i tial			_____
po ten tial			_____
torr en tial			_____
es pe ciall y			_____
ar ti fi cial			_____
con fi den tial			_____
sub stan tial			_____

Split the words into syllables. Sound out the syllables as you write them in the grey rectangles. Then write the whole word, saying the syllables as you do. This sheet may be photocopied by the purchaser. © Phonic Books Ltd. 2011.

Book 9: Splitting multisyllable words with 'shul' suffix 1b

Word	Syllables	Write
social	so | cial	social
facial		_____
racial		_____
partial		_____
special		_____
essential		_____
official		_____
initial		_____
potential		_____
torrential		_____
especially		_____
artificial		_____
confidential		_____
substantial		_____

Split the words into syllables. Sound out the syllables as you write them in the grey rectangles. Then write the whole word, saying the syllables as you do. This sheet may be photocopied by the purchaser. © Phonic Books Ltd. 2011.

Book 9: Splitting multisyllable words with 'shus' suffix 1a

pre cious	pre	cious	precious
cau tious			_____
nox ious			_____
con scious			_____
gra cious			_____
frac tious			_____
vi cious			_____
mal i cious			_____
aus pi cious			_____
sus pi cious			_____
viv a cious			_____
fer o cious			_____
de li cious			_____
ob nox ious			_____

Split the words into syllables. Sound out the syllables as you write them in the grey rectangles. Then write the whole word, saying the syllables as you do. This sheet may be photocopied by the purchaser. © Phonic Books Ltd. 2011.

Book 9: Splitting multisyllable words with 'shus' suffix 1b

precious	pre	cious		precious
cautious				_____
noxious				_____
conscious				_____
gracious				_____
fractious				_____
vicious				_____
malicious					_____
auspicious					_____
suspicious					_____
vivacious					_____
ferocious					_____
delicious					_____
obnoxious					_____

Split the words into syllables. Sound out the syllables as you write them in the grey rectangles. Then write the whole word, saying the syllables as you do. This sheet may be photocopied by the purchaser. © Phonic Books Ltd. 2011.

Book 9: Stepping stones game: 'shus' and 'shul'

START — **FINISH**

- martial
- delicious
- pretentious
- conscious
- official
- crucial
- spacious
- vicious
- tenacious
- social
- precious
- vivacious
- essential
- auspicious
- partial
- facial
- precocious
- gracious
- initial
- ferocious
- torrential
- special
- suspicious
- cautious
- malicious
- potential
- influential
- fictitious

This game is for 1–4 players. Play with counters and die. This sheet may be photocopied by the purchaser. © Phonic Books Ltd. 2011.

Book 9: 4-in-a-row game: 'shul'

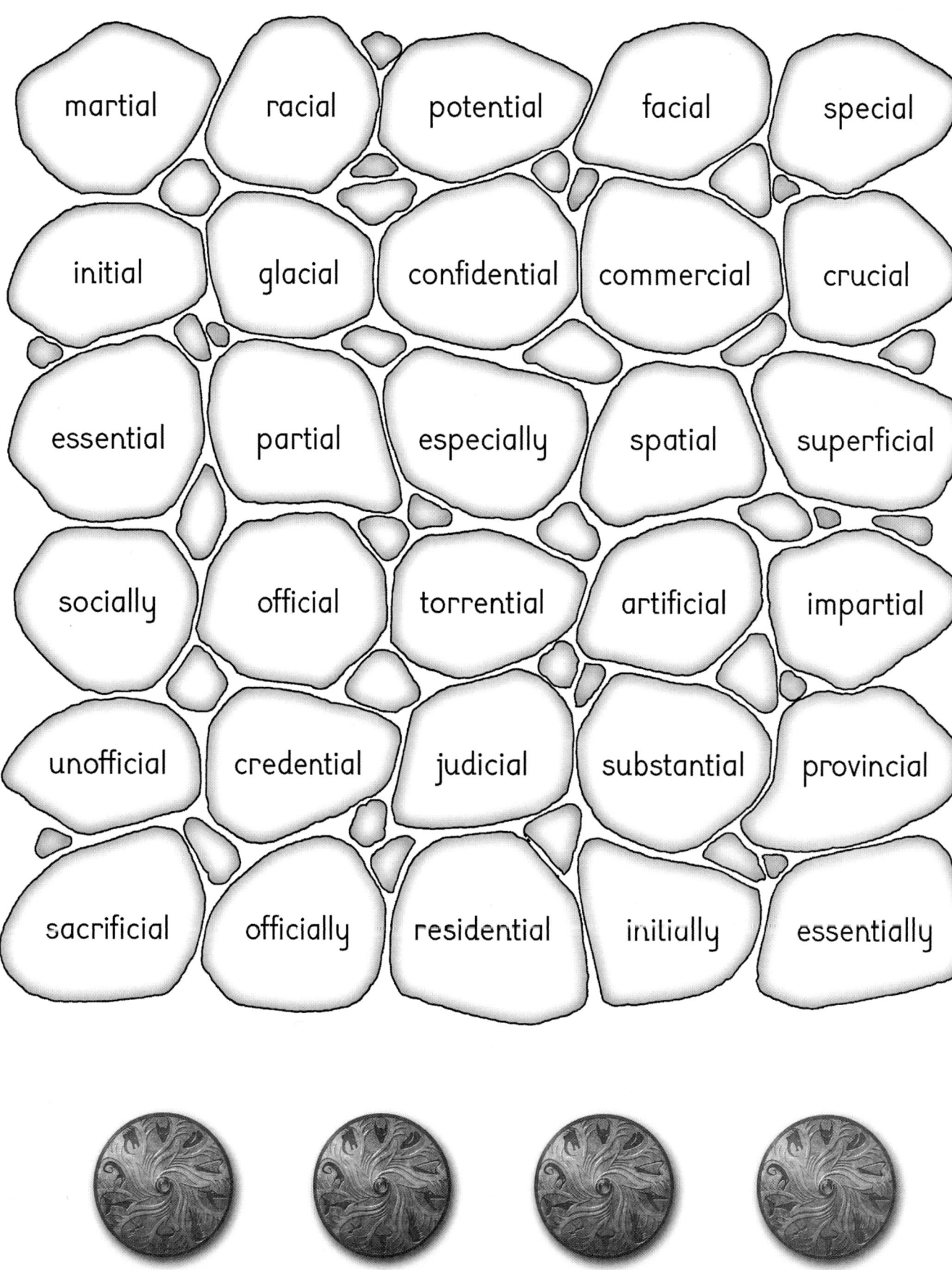

Play with two sets of coloured counters. Two players take turns to read the word and put a counter on the word. The winner is the first to get four of his or her counters in a row. The winner places a counter on a talisman. The game is played four times until all the talismans are covered. This sheet may be photocopied by the purchaser.
© Phonic Books Ltd. 2011.

Book 9: 4-in-a-row game: 'shus'

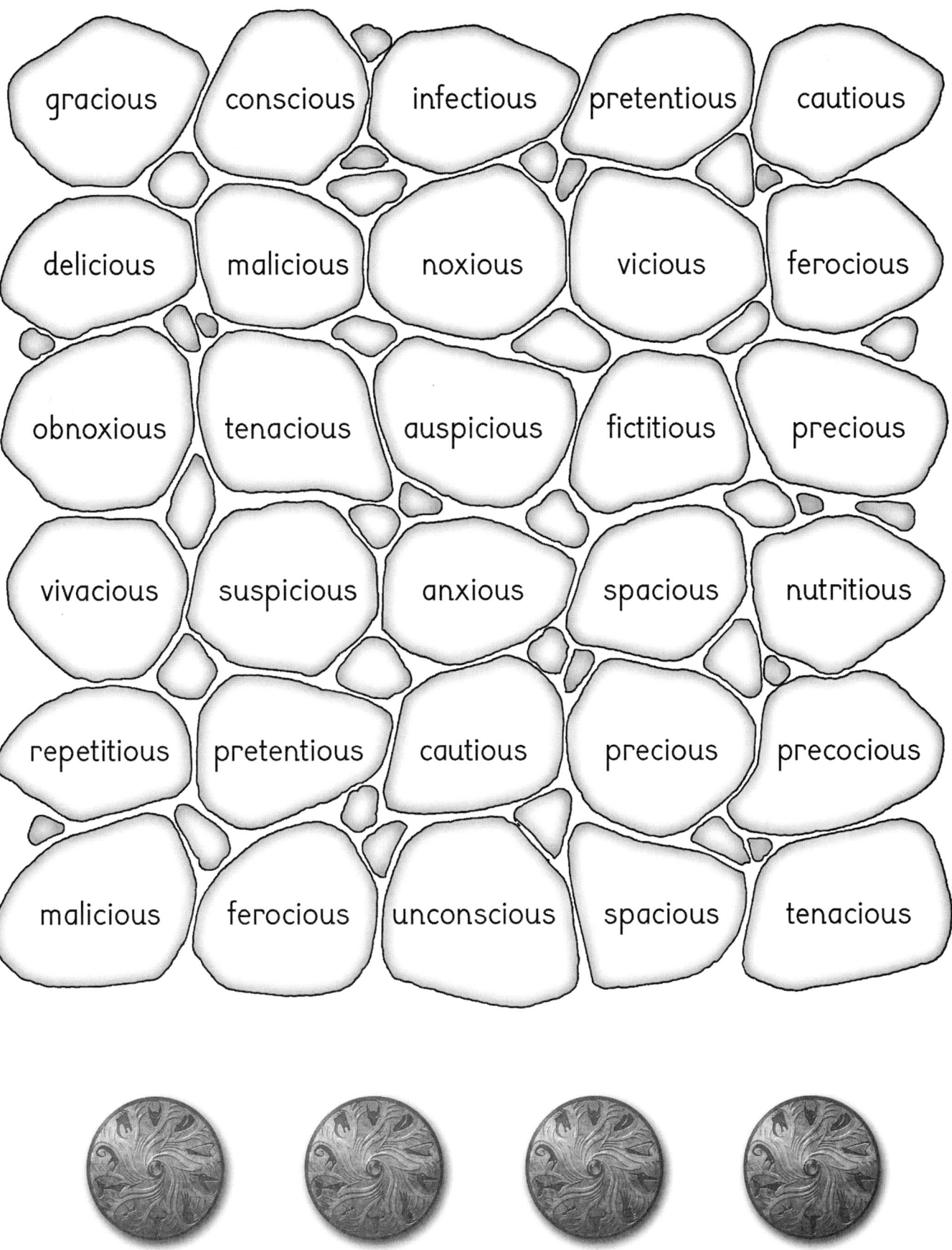

Play with two sets of coloured counters. Two players take turns to read the word and put a counter on the word. The winner is the first to get four of his or her counters in a row. The winner places a counter on a talisman. The game is played four times until all the talismans are covered. This sheet may be photocopied by the purchaser.
© Phonic Books Ltd. 2011.

Book 10: The Dark Master's Vision

Questions for discussion

Chapter 1

1. Why do you think Chapter 1 is called 'A Wonderful Occasion'? (pg 1)

2. What is an enclosure? (pg 1)

3. Why were there stones scattered everywhere? (pg 1)

Chapter 2

1. What was the Dark Master's vision? (pg 3)

2. Why was Zak surprised? (pg 4)

3. Why did he think his quest was a delusion? (pg 4)

Chapter 3

1. What was Leviathan's lethal weapon? (pg 7)

Chapter 4

1. Why did it take time for the talisman to make a decision? (pg 8)

2. Why did the Behemoth sound a trumpet call? (pg 9)

3. What happened when Leviathan attacked? (pg 10)

Chapter 5

1. What happened in the confusion of battle? (pg 11)

2. What do you think about the ending of the story? Explain. (pg 12)

These questions can be discussed after reading the text. They are intended to develop speaking and listening skills and comprehension. This sheet may be photocopied by the purchaser. © Phonic Books Ltd. 2011.

Book 10: Blending and segmenting: suffix 'zhun'

vision	v	i	sion	
division				
revision				
exclusion				
invasion				
confusion				
collision				
occasion				
fusion				
provision				
erosion				
explosion				
decision				

Blend the sounds into a word. Segment the word into sounds by writing one sound in each square.
This sheet may be photocopied by the purchaser.   © Phonic Books Ltd. 2011.

Book 10: Reading words with the suffix 'zhun' 1a

vision 1	confusion 2	revision 3	fusion 4
division 5	conclusion 6	precision 7	occasion 8
provision 9	collision 10	erosion 11	intrusion 12
decision 13	illusion 14	invasion 15	explosion 16
to make things stick together by heating them 4	being accurate 7	re-reading a subject before an exam 3	sharing out or dividing something 5
when things are mixed up, unclear 2	a special event or time 8	something that seems real but is not real 14	an unwelcome visit 12
food or supplies 9	wearing away of rocks 11	to make up one's mind 13	a crash 10
sight 1	invading with armed forces 15	a summing up of an argument 6	when something explodes 16

Photocopy this page onto card and cut out the words and the definitions. Match the definitions with the words, using the numbers and stick them back to back. Read the cards with the 'zhun' suffix. This sheet may be photocopied by the purchaser. © Phonic Books Ltd. 2011.

Book 10: Reading words with the suffix 'zhun' 1b

vision	confusion	revision	fusion
division	conclusion	precision	occasion
provision	collision	erosion	intrusion
decision	illusion	invasion	explosion
a summing up of an argument	a crash	re-reading a subject before an exam	when things are mixed up, unclear
sharing out or dividing something	to make things stick together by heating them	to make up one's mind	food or supplies
wearing away of rocks	an unwelcome visit	a special event or time	sight
something that seems real but is not real	when something explodes	invading with armed forces	being accurate

Photocopy this page onto card and cut out the words and the definitions. Match the definitions with the words and stick them back to back. Read the cards with the 'zhun' suffix. This sheet may be photocopied by the purchaser. © Phonic Books Ltd. 2011.

Book 10: Blending and segmenting: suffix 'zher'

measure	m	ea	sure		
leisure					
treasure					
pleasure					
closure					
exposure					
enclosure					
composure					
leisurely					
erasure					

Blend the sounds into a word. Segment the word into sounds by writing one sound in each square.
This sheet may be photocopied by the purchaser. © Phonic Books Ltd. 2011.

Book 10: Reading words with the suffix 'zher' 1a

treasure 1	measure 2	pleasure 3	leisure 4
exposure 5	disclosure 6	enclosure 7	composure 8
	closure 9	displeasure 10	

the act of closing something 9	being out in the open without protection 5	calmness 8	enjoyment 3
time that is free from work when you can do what you want 4	riches kept in a secret place 1	an area that is surrounded by a fence or a wall 7	to find out how big something is 2
	when someone is not pleased about something 10	giving information about something 6	

Photocopy this page onto card and cut out the words and the definitions. Match the definitions with the words, using the numbers and stick them back to back. Read the cards with the 'zher' suffix. This sheet may be photocopied by the purchaser. © Phonic Books Ltd. 2011.

Book 10: Reading words with the suffix 'zher' 1b

treasure	measure	pleasure	leisure
exposure	disclosure	enclosure	composure
	closure	displeasure	

the act of closing something	being out in the open without protection	to find out how big something is	time that is free from work when you can do what you want
calmness	riches kept in a secret place	an area that is surrounded by a fence or a wall	giving information about something
	enjoyment	when someone is not pleased about something	

Photocopy this page onto card and cut out the words and the definitions. Match the definitions with the words and stick them back to back. Read the cards with the 'zher' suffix. This sheet may be photocopied by the purchaser. © Phonic Books Ltd. 2011.

Book 10: Spelling with 'zhun' and 'zher'

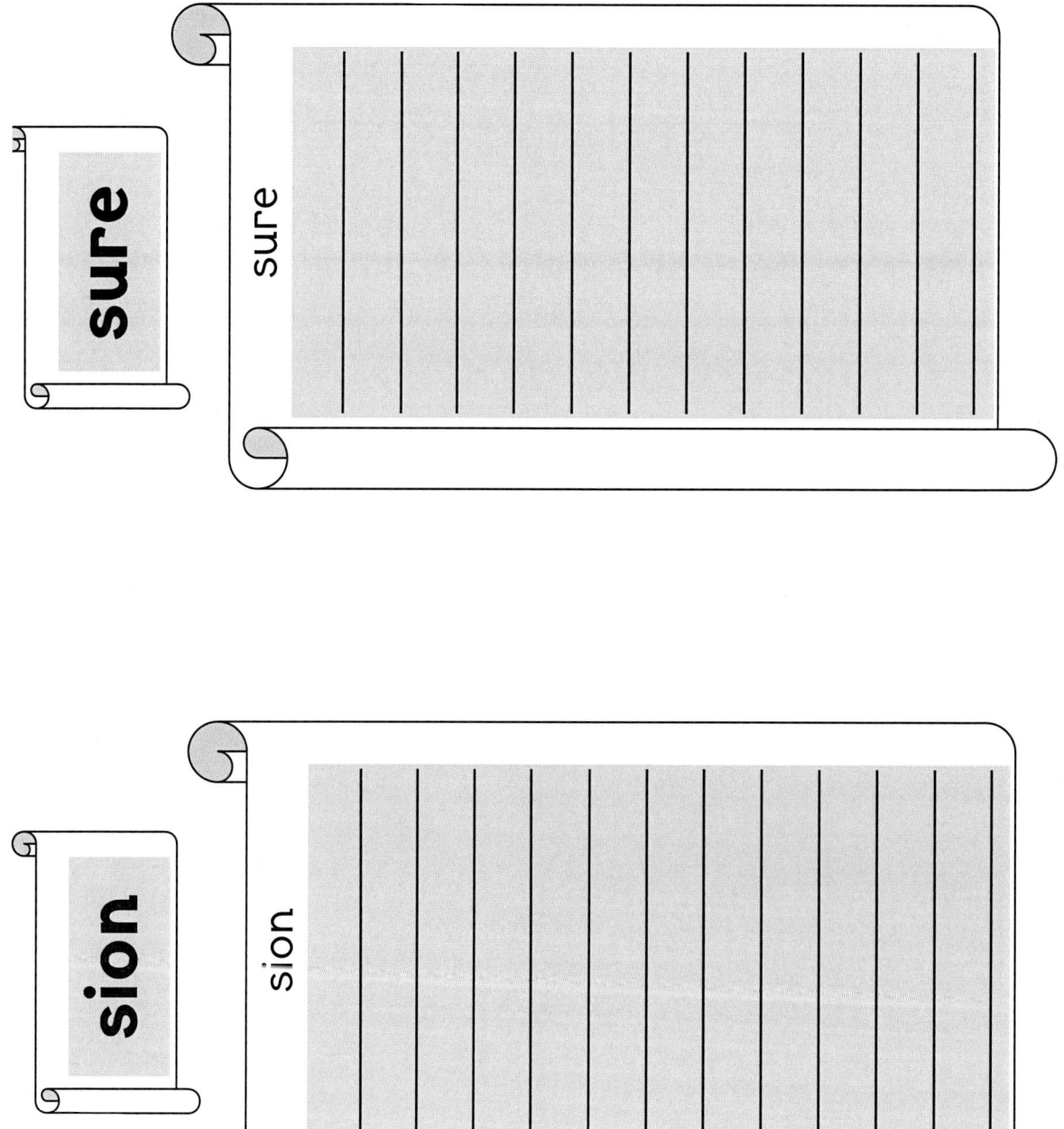

Read the text in Book 10, 'The Dark Master's Vision'. Find the words with the 'zhun' and 'zher' suffixes. List the words in the column. This sheet may be photocopied by the purchaser. © Phonic Books Ltd. 2011.

Book 10: Reading and spelling

The Dark Master stroked the new treasure in his hand. He said his vision had come to pass. Now that he had both talismans, he would destroy civilization. In the end, he was killed in a huge collision. This ended his vision.

The _ __ _   _ _ _ _ _
_ _ _ _ _ _   the   _ _
_ _ _ _   in his   _ _ _ _.
He _ _ _ _   _ _ _   _ _ _ _
_ _ _ _   _ _ _   to   _ _ _.
Now   _ _ _   he had   _ _ _
talismans, he would   _ _ _ _ _ _
_ _ _ _ _ _ _ _ _.   In the
end,   _ _   _ _ _   _ _ _ _
in a   _ _ _ _ _ _ _ _ _ _.
This   _ _ _ _ _   his   _ _ _ _.

Copy the text in the top scroll to the bottom scroll. Write a sound on each line e.g.: h i m. Where there is a target suffix, write the whole suffix on the line e.g.: v i sion. This activity can also be used for dictation. This sheet may be photocopied by the purchaser.
© Phonic Books Ltd. 2011.

Book 10: Is it true?

How many untruths can you spot in the text?

Zak and Mim came to an enclosure. The Dark Master stood in the middle, like a haunted vision. He held his new treasure. Suddenly, Zak and Mim were trapped in a net. The Dark Master shape shifted into a Leviathan. Its tail sliced the air with precision. An explosion sent Mim and Zak into the air in slow motion. Then Zak shape shifted into a Behemoth creature. It grabbed Leviathan leisurely in its strong claws. In a mighty collision, Leviathan was impaled on Behemoth's tusk. Zak and Mim made a decision to throw one talisman into the sea and keep the other for future adventures.

How many untruths did you find?

Read this text after reading Book 10, 'The Dark Master's Vision'. Underline the parts which are not true to the story in the book. Count the untruths and write the number in the box. This sheet may be photocopied by the purchaser. © Phonic Books Ltd. 2011.

Book 10: Writing 1

The mighty battle – what was it like?

Leviathan's tail was like:
a guillotine
a blade
a machete

Behemoth's skin was like:
armour
leather
chain mail

Leviathan attacked like a:
water dragon
terrifying crocodile
dangerous shark

The mighty collision was like:
an earthquake
an explosion
a volcano erupting

Describe the mighty battle:
_____
_____
_____
_____
_____
_____
_____

Describe the mighty battle between the Leviathan and Behemoth. You can use some of the words in the boxes. This sheet may be photocopied by the purchaser. © Phonic Books Ltd. 2011.

Book 10: Splitting multisyllable words with 'zhun' suffix 1a

vi sion	vi	sion	<u>vision</u>
fu sion			_____
ver sion			_____
re vi sion			_____
de ci sion			_____
pro vi sion			_____
pre ci sion			_____
div i sion			_____
coll i sion			_____
con fu sion			_____
in va sion			_____
occ a sion			_____
trans fu sion			_____
e ro sion			_____

Split the words into syllables. Sound out the syllables as you write them in the grey rectangles. Then write the whole word, saying the syllables as you do. This sheet may be photocopied by the purchaser. © Phonic Books Ltd. 2011.

Book 10: Splitting multisyllable words with 'zhun' suffix 1b

vision   vi | sion   <u>vision</u>

fusion   ☐ | ☐   _____

version   ☐ | ☐   _____

revision   ☐ | ☐ | ☐   _____

decision   ☐ | ☐ | ☐   _____

provision   ☐ | ☐ | ☐   _____

precision   ☐ | ☐ | ☐   _____

division   ☐ | ☐ | ☐   _____

collision   ☐ | ☐ | ☐   _____

confusion   ☐ | ☐ | ☐   _____

invasion   ☐ | ☐ | ☐   _____

occasion   ☐ | ☐ | ☐   _____

transfusion   ☐ | ☐ | ☐   _____

erosion   ☐ | ☐ | ☐   _____

Split the words into syllables. Sound out the syllables as you write them in the grey rectangles. Then write the whole word, saying the syllables as you do. This sheet may be photocopied by the purchaser. © Phonic Books Ltd. 2011.

Book 10: Splitting multisyllable words with 'zher' suffix 1a

mea sure	mea	sure	measure
trea sure			_____
lei sure			_____
plea sure			_____
clo sure			_____
en clo sure			_____
ex po sure			_____
com po sure			_____
lei sure ly			_____
dis clo sure			_____
e ra sure			_____

Split the words into syllables. Sound out the syllables as you write them in the grey rectangles. Then write the whole word, saying the syllables as you do. This sheet may be photocopied by the purchaser. © Phonic Books Ltd. 2011.

Book 10: Splitting multisyllable words with 'zher' suffix 1b

measure	mea	sure	<u>measure</u>
treasure			_____
leisure			_____
pleasure			_____
closure			_____
enclosure			_____
exposure			_____
composure			_____
leisurely			_____
disclosure			_____
erasure			_____

Split the words into syllables. Sound out the syllables as you write them in the grey rectangles. Then write the whole word, saying the syllables as you do. This sheet may be photocopied by the purchaser. © Phonic Books Ltd. 2011.

Book 10: Writing activity 2

Book review of the Talisman 2 Series

What did you like about the Talisman 2 Series?

_____

_____

_____

_____

What would you change about the series?

_____

_____

_____

_____

Did you think it was suitable for your age? Why?

_____

_____

_____

_____

Would you recommend it to your friends? Why?

_____

_____

Book 10: Writing activity 3

Talisman 3 Series – Chapter 1

Talisman 2 Series ended with Zak and Mim hurling both the talismans in the deep blue sea.

If you were to write the next series, how would you start it? What happens in the depths of the sea? Who are your heroes? Zak and Mim or new characters? Will they go on a quest? Why?

Write the first chapter of the series.

_____

_____

_____

_____

_____

_____

_____

_____

_____

_____

_____

_____

_____

_____

Book 10: Stepping stones game: 'zhun' and 'zher'

START

- vision
- decision
- revision
- confusion
- illusion
- closure
- precision
- disclosure
- measure
- explosion
- enclosure
- division
- collision
- treasure
- erosion
- intrusion
- conclusion
- exposure
- leisure
- erasure
- incision
- delusion
- infusion
- inclusion
- fusion
- invasion
- pleasure
- occasion

FINISH

Book 10: 4-in-a-row game: 'zhun' and 'zher'

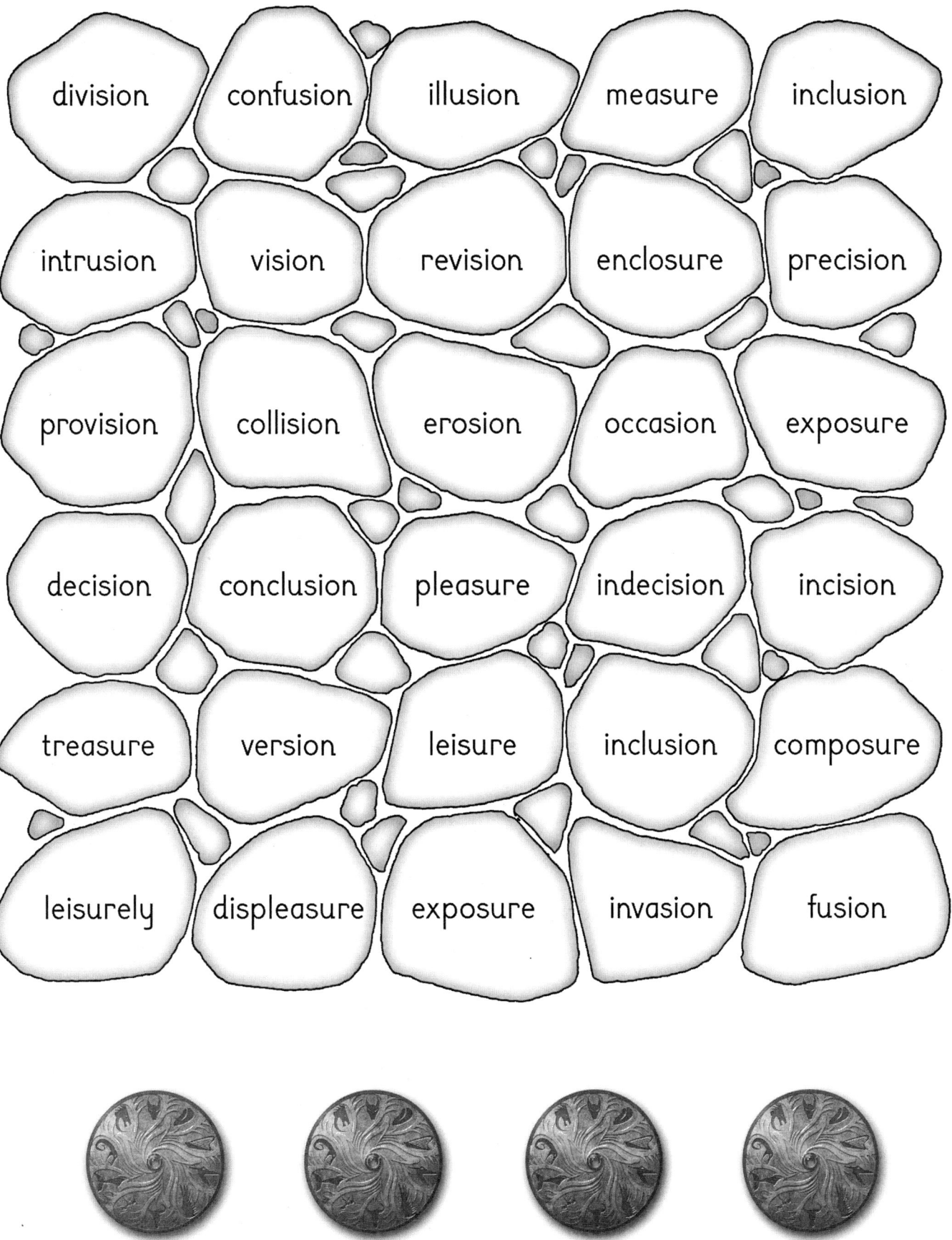

Play with two sets of coloured counters. Two players take turns to read the word and put a counter on the word. The winner is the first to get four of his or her counters in a row. The winner places a counter on a talisman. The game is played four times until all the talismans are covered. This sheet may be photocopied by the purchaser.
© Phonic Books Ltd. 2011.